FOR MY MOTHER

Admiral Byrd of Antarctica

Born: October 25, 1888

Died: March 11, 1957

An exciting biography of America's most famous polar explorer. He piloted the first airmail flight across the Atlantic, and later beat Amundsen's dirigible in a race to the North Pole. Admiral Byrd made five expeditions to the Antarctic, setting up permanent bases for scientific study, and opened up five million miles of eerie white wilderness. He spent seven harrowing months alone at an advance base, out of touch with anyone. For his contribution to Antarctic expeditions, he was awarded the Medal of Freedom in 1957.

Admiral Byrd of Antarctica

by
Michael Gladych

Julian Messner   New York

Published simultaneously in the United States and Canada by
Julian Messner, a division of Simon & Schuster, Inc.,
1 West 39 Street, New York, N.Y. 10018. All rights reserved.

Seventh Printing, 1968

Printed in the United States of America

Library of Congress Catalog Card No. 60–7053

THE BOY FLATTENED HIS TENSE, LITHE BODY AGAINST the moist earth of the dugout, then cautiously lifted his head and peered over the fort's parapet. Somewhere in the bushes, fifty paces away, lurked the enemy.

He squinted his blue-gray eyes against the hot Virginia sun, vainly trying to penetrate the thick foliage. If only the breeze would abate, he thought. The rustle of those big elms drowned the giveaway sounds—a broken twig or a careless footstep.

Then he remembered an old Indian trick he had read about. Without looking he reached for a pile of stones— his ammunition supply. Selecting a hefty rock, he expertly hurled it into the thicket. The stone swooshed through the branches and landed with a soft thud.

From the far side of the garden a voice rang out. "I see where you are, Dick. I'm coming after you!"

Dick Byrd chuckled inwardly, watching the swaying bushes in the wake of his brother Tom. The trick worked. He sprang up and darted into the shrubs, pouncing from behind upon the unsuspecting Tom.

But a low branch, covered by last year's dry leaves, foiled the perfect flank attack. Dick stumbled and sprawled headlong only a few feet behind his prey. Before he could recover Tom landed on top of him, pinning him down. Taller and heavier than his older brother, Tom now commanded the situation.

"Give up, Dick?"

Dick only squirmed, panting.

"You haven't got a chance. . . . Surrender!"

The smaller boy shook his head. His jugular vein swelled and knotted on the sides of his neck. His tanned face reddened from the strain. Suddenly his wiry body went limp.

Surprised, Tom momentarily relaxed his grip. In half-a-heartbeat Dick pulled his knees under his brother's body and uncoiled them with a mighty push. Tom let go. As he sailed through the air, his arms outstretched, Dick was up —diving after him and reaching for his throat.

Dick's powerful fingers locked in a strangle hold. Tom kicked, wriggled desperately, trying to break the choking grip. The boys rolled in the underbrush, gasping and moaning, spitting the leaves.

"Tom . . . Dick . . . where are you?"

Oblivious of the world around them, the boys wrestled until their older brother, Harry, found them. With a half-nelson he pried Dick off, then shook him by the shoulders. "Look at you," he said, gasping. "You, too, Tom—you're a sight."

Tom sat up, wiping his sweaty face with his sleeve. "You aren't exactly dressed for church yourself," he said. "What happened to you?"

Harry touched his bruised cheek. "Ouch! I guess I didn't feel it during the battle." He squatted and tugged at his sleeve, almost torn off at the seam. "I was ambushed," he said apologetically.

Tom and Dick exchanged glances. "Tater Hill gang?"

Harry nodded.

Tom stood up. "Well, what are we waiting for? Let's go!"

"Not so fast." Dick shook his head. "We're outnumbered ten to one. We need a plan. Come on, we'll talk it over in the fort."

They squatted in the dugout, Indian fashion. Dick took a piece of broken twig, smoothed the earth with the sole of his shoe, and began to sketch the battle map. "We'll go up Braddock Street," he said, "approach them from the rear. They must not see us. Remember what Captain Carson used to tell us about the Spanish War? Surprise is half the battle won—"

"Sure," Harry interrupted. "But even though we surprise them, how do you propose to win even half the fight? There are three of us against thirty of them. Jake said his two cousins are coming this afternoon from Shenandoah. We haven't got a chance—we must get some reinforcements!"

Dick snapped the twig he held. "You'll make an excellent prosecuting attorney, just like Father. You sure can paint a gloomy picture. But fighting the Tater Hill gang is a matter of family honor. If we don't avenge the beating you took this afternoon, we'll never be able to

9

show our faces anywhere in Winchester. Therefore we must take a chance. And even a county prosecutor gambles sometimes. Remember how Father brought fifty armed mountaineers to court singlehanded?"

"That's right," Tom chimed in. "If Father did it, we can do it too. Let's fight the gang!"

Outvoted, Harry nodded his assent while Dick—a thirteen-year-old "general"—explained his battle plan. First they would reconnoiter the situation, and wait until the Tater Hill gang assembled in force for their usual afternoon ball game on the vacant lot next to Jake's house. Then, at a signal, the three of them would form a wedge and charge downhill. They would aim at Jake—knock him out.

Dick gesticulated. "With Jake down and nobody to give them orders, they'll get confused. We'll fight all we can—stir up a big commotion. And when we think they've had enough, we'll withdraw honorably."

The three brothers crouched under the French windows of their father's study and then walked briskly up Amherst Street. Just as they were passing General Morgan's house, a girl's voice called out, "Dick, wait for me!"

Dick blushed under his brothers' stare. Slowing down a little, he waved to a pretty blonde girl. "I can't, Marie. This is family business. Be back in a little while."

He caught up with his brothers and, still blushing, murmured by way of apology, "Women . . ."

They followed the plan scrupulously. The Tater Hill gang was there, as expected, with Jake bossing everybody around. On a signal the Byrd boys sprinted, picked up more speed downhill, and charged among the enemy.

But instead of waiting to be knocked out by the first

impact of the Byrd "wedge," Jake side-stepped and the well-planned tactic fizzled—there was nobody to mow down. Gasping from the charge, the three boys found themselves surrounded by the gang with Jake still in command.

The brothers instinctively pulled together, back to back, in perfect boxing stance, just as their father had taught them. Tight-lipped, their nostrils flaring, they waited for the inevitable attack.

However, Jake didn't give his usual "git 'em" command. Towering over the rest of his "army," he said, "I want three volunteers. This is gonna be fair 'n' square— three of us agin three of them." He scanned his ranks, and when no volunteers were forthcoming he planted his bare feet wide apart and bellowed, "You dirty yellow-bellies . . . you skunkheads. Git! You hear? Git—all of you. I'll fight them myself!"

Jake's warriors, chastised in front of the hopelessly outnumbered enemy, cowered and began to disperse. But morbid curiosity as to the result of the forthcoming engagement brought them together again. As though anxious lest the Byrd boys try to escape and thus cheat them of a promising spectacle, they closed their ranks into a circle.

The Byrd brothers quickly regrouped, like a well-disciplined football team. Harry and Tom flanked Dick— all of them ready to box. It was a reflex action, born of many scraps fought shoulder to shoulder.

Jake focused intently on his three opponents. He advanced slowly, haltingly. He flayed his long bony arms in huge circles, like two windmills. This was his trademark—the "haymaker" which won him the reputation

11

of being a fearless fighter in Winchester. In fact, some of the Tater Hill gang bragged that Jake's name was known all over Virginia.

It was so quiet that you could hear the ominous swish of Jake's big fists. Against this tense silence Dick's voice rang out.

"Wait, Jake!" Dick jumped forward, meeting the bigger boy halfway. "You're outnumbered—it's not fair. I'll fight you alone."

Probably taken aback by his small opponent's unexpected spunk, Jake stopped his shuffling advance. His arms dropped to his sides. The two, now within easy striking distance, faced each other—a wiry David and a bony Goliath.

The gang gasped, rubbernecking, closing their circle.

Shaking his head in utter disbelief, Jake leaned over his adversary until his freckled face came within an inch of Dick's. "You ain't afeared of me?" he asked.

Dick swallowed hard. "No," he said, tightening his fists until the knuckles showed white.

Jake hitched his pants with his elbows and stared into Dick's blue-gray eyes. Then he shook his head again. "Well, I guess you ain't, at that," he drawled, wiping his open palm on the seat of his faded trousers. "No use fightin' then—let's shake on it."

Slowly, as though suspecting a trap, Dick unclenched his right fist and grasped the bigger boy's hand with all his strength.

A murmur of hostile disappointment ran through the Tater Hill gang. Done out of what could have been a breath-taking show, they made ready to rush the Byrds. A squatty, curly-haired boy, his clothes covered with

patches—campaign ribbons of countless battles—
shouted, "Come on, let's git 'em!"

But Jake was in command of the situation. He took
one step toward the mutineer. "You had your chance.
Now shut up. Quiet, all of you!" The mob was silent
again, and Jake turned to his erstwhile enemy with a
clumsy gesture of welcome. "You can come to Tater Hill
any time," he said. "An' you can come sledding in the
winter, too." With great ceremony he shook Harry's
hand, then Tom's.

The three boys looked at one another and nodded ac-
ceptance of the unexpected peace offering. Without
further delay they triumphantly marched off the lot, followed by the bewildered stares of the Tater Hill gang.

For three blocks they walked in silence—still under
the spell of their bloodless victory. Then Harry spoke.
"That was a little foolish of you, Dick. Suppose he had
accepted the challenge."

"I was pretty sure he wouldn't," Dick said. "Besides,
he doesn't know how to box. That haymaker is strictly
for the birds."

The pun on their name touched off a spontaneous outburst of laughter. The brothers linked their arms and
strutted down Braddock Street like the Three Musketeers.

Instead of approaching their large stucco house from
Amherst Street, the boys detoured through the woods.
They followed a path by the railroad tracks and, unseen
by their parents, emerged at their fort. There they expertly tidied themselves, removing all traces of the earlier
fights. This routine was wisely instituted by Harry some
time ago and, as he had said, "spared their mother need-
less worry."

Holding a handful of cool elm leaves to his bruised cheek, Harry said, "Don't forget to enter today's date in big red letters in your diary, Dick—Monday, August 13, 1902 A.D.—declaration of peace with the Tater Hill gang." He stood up and raised his free hand. "May peace reign forever in our quiet town of Winchester, Commonwealth of Virginia," he said with mock seriousness.

"Amen to that," Tom joined in. "Except . . . what are we going to do the rest of the summer vacation?"

Dick was not listening to his brothers. His keen ears detected a distant, throaty whistle and the hurried chugging of a train engine. Whenever he heard that call, his mind conjured up exciting scenes from faraway lands he had read about: the Gold Coast of Africa . . . the jungle of Sumatra . . . places untouched by railroads and civilization. Someday he would travel there. He would reach where no other human had dared to reach.

His heart speeded up as the train came closer. The slight tremor of earth under his feet sent an exciting shiver up through his lithe body. He could almost smell the tingling fragrance the iron brake shoes make when they grip the train's wheels, grinding them to a stop.

"Hey, Dick, this calls for a real council of war," Harry said. "What *are* we going to do?"

Still not quite back from his dream world, Dick answered quietly, "I'm going to explore—"

"Explore what?" Harry chuckled. "Don't tell me you want to go back to the Staunton caves and the Lost River. You fell asleep exploring that one, remember?"

The freight train came to a jangling stop. The engine let out a hissing blast of steam and panted rhythmically as though tired after the long haul.

"Sure," Tom joined in. "Remember? All the neighbors were looking for you and Mother was worried sick. I don't think exploring is so good. Let's think of something else. Say, how about asking Father to organize another target practice?"

His dreams now gone, Dick perked up to the idea. "Wonderful! He did promise to let us fire his six-shooter this summer. We can have a competition—see who is the fastest on the draw. We'll make the targets tonight. Come on, let's ask him about it!"

The boys galloped to the side entrance, halted respectfully before the door to their father's study, and let Harry knock.

"Come in!"

They tiptoed into the study and stood silently before the large desk strewn with papers. Richard E. Byrd, Sr. looked at them over his gold-rimmed glasses. "Well now, this is quite a coincidence. I was about to call you, Dick." He reached to a stack of mail. "Here is a letter for you from Judge Carson, from the Philippines."

Dick took the envelope, battered by the thousands of miles of travel. "Master Richard Evelyn Byrd, Jr.," read the address. He held it gingerly, as though it were a great and fragile treasure.

"Father, we were going to ask you about the pistol practice," he said. "But may I please read this first?"

"Of course. And save the stamps, will you?"

Forgetting protocol, Dick didn't even excuse himself. He burst out of the study and ran upstairs to his bedroom, where he carefully opened the envelope and read.

"I have never forgotten my promise to you," wrote Judge Adam ("Kit") C. Carson. "At first, after my arrival here, things were much too lively—the *ladrones* who refused to surrender launched large-scale attacks and our existence was rather precarious, even in Manila. However, the situation seems to be under control now and I feel it would be safe for you to visit me. Of course, there is still much excitement . . ."

Dick did not read further. He hurriedly folded the letter, shoved it into his shirt pocket, and rushed out. He slid down the polished banister and almost tumbled down the porch steps in his hurry to mount his bicycle. His heart pounding from excitement, he pedaled down the street.

Miss Lizzy Sharon, his former teacher from the elementary Boys' School, was puttering around her flower beds. Dick skidded his bike to a stop and, without dismounting, called to her.

"I'm going to Manila—to the Philippines. I'll write you all the news, Miss Lizzy. Good-bye!"

He stopped at Marie Ames' house and at his aunt's, Mrs. Joe Massie's . . . he hunted up all his friends. To everyone he told the same incoherent, exciting story. When he finally returned home, it was dark.

Weak-kneed from exertion and joy, he sneaked into the house to find the family at the dinner table.

"I think you owe us an explanation for being late," said Mr. Byrd, Sr.

Tom giggled. "I bet he's been to see Marie and forgot the time."

Mr. Byrd gave Tom a stern look and the boy shrank into his chair, red-faced.

"Well, Dick?"

16

"I'm very sorry, Father," Dick said, taking his place at the table. "I was saying good-bye to my friends."

"Yes . . ."

"Well, I . . ." Dick fumbled for the letter. "Uncle Kit Carson invited me to visit him. I think you'd better read this, Father."

Mr. Byrd, Sr., adjusted his glasses and smoothed the crumpled letter with the palm of his hand. He finished reading, folded the letter carefully, and returned it to Dick. "I suggest you write the Judge and thank him at once—"

Dick could not contain himself. "Hurray!"

"Richard." Mr. Byrd did not raise his voice, but there was an iron toughness to his tone. "You are at the table, don't forget. Secondly, your outburst was premature. You are not going anywhere, except to school, of course —the Shenandoah Valley Academy."

"But, Father—"

"There will be time for any discussion of the matter after dinner."

Dick could not swallow a bite. He simply had to make Father understand . . . he had to go. Besides, how could he stay now that he had told everybody he was going?

The dinner over, Dick resolutely followed his father to his study, carefully closing the door behind him. For over an hour he pleaded his case, but his father's mind seemed to be made up. The Philippines were no place for a thirteen-year-old boy. The newspapers daily reported skirmishes between the United States Marines and the natives, he told Dick. Perhaps in a few years the situation would change for the better, but now the trip was out of the question.

Desperate, but not giving up, Dick let his father make the objections. When Mr. Byrd finished, Dick drew himself up. "Father, I wouldn't go against your will, of course." His voice trembled. "But if you don't let me go, I shall never forgive you as long as I live."

Mr. Byrd got up slowly, came from behind his desk and put both his hands on Dick's shoulders. "If this is how much that voyage means to you, you may go," he said calmly. "I shall speak to your mother about it."

2

THE TIME PASSED QUICKLY IN VARIOUS PREPARATIONS
for the ten-thousand-mile trip. In fact, there were moments when Dick wanted to slow down the clock for
reasons not known even to him. The night before his
departure, he sat in his room and fondled the sheaf of
rail and steamship tickets adorned with faraway names
that spelled adventure—San Francisco, Nagasaki, Manila. He had to tell himself that this was not another of
his dreams; the tickets were real and tomorrow he would
be on a train—Dick Byrd, the traveler.

Having gone over the list of things he and his mother
had packed in the large leather bag Mr. Byrd had contributed, Dick headed the family procession down the
front-porch steps. They arrived at the station in plenty
of time. In fact, Dick felt the 11:05 train for Washington would never come.

The last few minutes dragged like rainy days. Mrs. Byrd covertly dabbed at her nose with a handkerchief and Mr. Byrd cleared his throat as though he were going to say something. Jake, Hink, and several other members of the Tater Hill gang gaped at the family group from a respectful distance, and the telegraph man kept shaking his head in the station's bay window.

Finally the train chugged in. A wet kiss from Mother and a hard embrace from Father, brief handshakes with Harry and Tom, a timid "Good luck, Dick" from Jake . . . Dick climbed into a car. Jake sidled to Tom. "Lookit, he's crying," he said.

Tom grabbed the bigger boy's shirt front. "Dick isn't crying. That's poison oak he got into yesterday."

The train jerked forward. His face glued to the window, Dick noticed a slim blonde girl waving to him from behind the crowd. "Good-bye, Marie," he whispered. "I'll be back soon." The little station disappeared from view. Reluctantly Dick sat down. His throat felt strangely tight, just like that time on Tater Hill when he stepped up to face Jake.

The worst part of the trip was to Washington. Dick had been there before and the familiarity of the landscape was like a stiff breeze, trying to push him back to Winchester. But the skyscrapers of New York City, then the sight of Chicago and the newness of the life on board the speeding train quickly gave the boy a strange kind of confidence.

There was an uncomfortable moment or two when the fellow passengers good-naturedly ribbed Dick about the large tag on his jacket with his itinerary hand-printed by Mrs. Byrd. But by the time the train rolled into San

Francisco, Dick could only think of the sea voyage and the Philippine jungle. He tipped the porter a silver dollar, and felt every inch a seasoned globe-trotter.

He was quite indignant when the purser of the *SS Sumner* asked in an incredulous voice, "You are alone . . . sir?"

Dick stretched himself to his full four feet eight. "Of course," he said, trying to imitate the sailors' gait as he walked up the gangplank.

At the end of the first day at sea, Dick hid his itinerary tag at the bottom of his suitcase. Within three days he made friends with the chief engineer, knew all the stokers by name, and could tell by the manometers when the boilers needed more coal.

In a week he became the only passenger allowed on the bridge and into the chart room, where he spent hours watching Mr. MacDonald, the first mate, plot the ship's course. The mystery of navigation absorbed Dick more than anything else. He pestered the burly first mate until he was allowed to "shoot" the sun position one noon with the ship's sextant.

Bracing himself against the pitch and roll of the deck, Dick handed the sextant back to Mr. MacDonald. "If what this instrument measures is the angle between the sun and the horizon," Dick said, "what happens if the horizon is covered with mist or haze?"

The first mate rubbed his bulbous nose. "Well, you wait for better weather."

"Only because of a lttle haze?"

"That's right. Of course you can always dead-reckon—"

"But that's kind of guessing at your position."

21

MacDonald put the sextant into its plush-lined case. "You may call it that, I guess." Then, a little impatiently, he said, "It's pretty accurate, though. And if you don't think so, wait till we hit Nagasaki—right on the nose. If you're not satisfied then—well, you'd better figure out a better sextant."

Following MacDonald into the chart room, Dick watched the first mate tap the barometer and frown. "Anything wrong, sir?" he asked.

The man nodded gravely. "Could be." He tapped the glass again. "The barometer's dropping like a lead *sonde*. That and the color of the sun make me think we're heading for a storm—a real tough one, or my name isn't MacDonald."

"Couldn't we by-pass it?"

MacDonald shook his head. "We're not fast enough. We'll just batten down the hatches and get ready. We'll make it, all right."

That night, feeling the gentle motion of his berth, Dick decided to study mathematics, navigation, and meteorology. Someday he would sail ships that could by-pass storms. Maybe he would even make a sextant that worked all the time, haze or not.

He awoke with a painful jolt. Groping in the dark cabin, he realized that he had been tossed out of his warm berth. The ship groaned, pitched, and rolled in a sickening motion.

Dick crawled to the door and, bracing himself with one hand, reached for the brass match box fastened to the wall. After several trials he managed to light the lamp.

The cabin was filled with strange animation. Dick's

22

suitcase, his diary, and his clothes slid to and fro as though bent upon measuring the cabin's skimpy floor space over and over again. Bewildered, but realizing that the ship was being battered by a storm, Dick dressed hurriedly.

As soon as he turned the knob, the door burst open. The wind blew out the lamp and filled Dick's lungs till he gasped for breath. Deafened by the gale, hanging to the handrails, slipping and stumbling, he made his way to the bridge.

It was relatively quiet inside, although the wooden walls creaked as though ready to collapse under the wind pressure. The helmsman and Mr. MacDonald wrestled with the steering wheel. The faint glow of the compass light cast deep, grotesque shadows on their tense faces. Wedged in one corner of the wheelhouse, the captain peered through the spray-smeared windows into the howling darkness ahead.

Dick inched his way to him. "Quite a storm, sir."

"Storm? My boy, it's a full-blasted typhoon!"

Dick had read about the China Sea typhoons that appeared out of nowhere and swallowed hundreds of ships only to spit out smashed flotsam—weeks, perhaps months, later. He felt a tight knot tugging heavily in the pit of his stomach and found himself holding his breath until the pounding in his ears muffled the gale outside. But as soon as he exhaled, he was aware of a strange excitement. His feet, firmly planted against the deck, felt a tremor of the ship's structure that filled him with a scintillating warmth he could scarcely understand. It was as though he were a part of this gallant ship built of tough, resilient steel, shaking off the angry mountains of water and spume—confident in its own strength, unafraid.

Tugging at the captain's sleeve, Dick said, "Anything I can do?"

A flash of lightning filled the wheelhouse with an eerie whiteness. For a split second the captain's tense face softened. "Sure, my boy," he boomed. "Get down to the main salon and take care of the passengers . . . they must be having kittens by now. Tell 'em there's nothing to worry about—we're going to pull through. Off you go, *Mister* Byrd!"

The main cabin was a bedlam. The wildly swinging oil lamps flickered, then flared hysterically. In one corner somebody intoned "Nearer my God to Thee." A woman tore at a porthole and screamed, "They have bolted us in! I'm suffocating! Open the windows. Help . . . help!" Another held her baby to her bosom and stared wide-eyed at an imaginary point in space. A man in a business jacket buttoned tight over his underwear demanded to see the captain. "I'll sue him and the company! This is gross incompetence! I'll have him blacklisted!"

Nauseated by the stench of perspiration and kerosene fumes, Dick made his way to the screaming woman and firmly grasped her wrist. "Madam," he said sternly, "those bolted covers are for your own safety. But we are not locked in. Would you like to go outside with me?"

Bumping into fellow passengers, Dick led the woman to the door. As he turned the knob a wave boarded the ship and rammed the door open, drenching the hysterical woman and several other people in the cabin. Dick put his shoulder to the door and closed it.

Shivering from the unexpected cold shower, the woman

stammered, "I d-don't want t-to go out in that storm . . . just let me s-sit in my corner."

Dick left her. He circulated through the cabin from passenger to passenger, explaining, soothing, and helping. Inspired by his example, the men organized a "calm-down" committee. Women were made more comfortable, somebody got to the piano and started a sing-song, and a group of volunteers took turns in bringing hot tea from the galley.

Hours later, when Mr. MacDonald came to announce that the worst was over, the passengers couldn't say enough about "that Byrd boy" who in his quiet way radiated courage and confidence.

"Well, he'll make a fine mariner someday," MacDonald said, patting Dick on the back. "Yes, sir."

The typhoon delayed them by four days but, in spite of being late, the *SS Sumner* made Nagasaki "right on the nose," as MacDonald had predicted. "You see, even the guesswork of dead reckoning is quite a science," he told Dick. "It's always knowing where you've been that helps you to figure where you're going."

"Even in a storm?" Dick said.

MacDonald smiled. "Well, not really. But if you batten down the hatches and head for deep water where you have plenty of leeway—get ready for the worst—you can weather anything. You know you'll make your port, just as I know now that we'll be in Manila seven days from now, God willing."

The eventful sea voyage ended far too quickly for Dick. He made his final tour of the ship, saying good-bye to everyone—from the captain to the last oiler in the engine room. He lingered at the head of the gangplank

25

until he saw a tall white-clad man standing in a carriage and waving his Panama hat.

"Captain Carson! Kit!" Dick rushed down to meet the old family friend.

"Wonderful to see you, Dick." Carson made a sweeping gesture. "Welcome to the Philippines! And, incidentally, I am no longer a captain. Call me Judge, or Kit."

"But you do carry a gun," Dick said, pointing to the Army pistol.

"Self-protection. You'll have to have one, too. Things are still far from peaceful, so I keep my eyes on my lawbooks and my hand on the gun."

As the carriage trundled along Boniface Drive, Carson and Dick exchanged news, the latter taking in the exotic sights of the city—the historic Intramuros district walled in by the Spaniards, the churches, and native houses of nipa and bamboo.

"You've grown tremendously this past year," Carson said, feeling Dick's biceps. "Remember the parade in front of President McKinley in Washington? Why, you could hardly lift my pistol then, and look at you now!" Carson slapped Dick on the back. "Well, just get a good night's sleep and tomorrow we'll outfit you. You might even go on a mission or two with our constabulary force —see how you like the jungle and the insurrection."

In spite of heat and humidity, Dick slept like a log and the Filipino servant almost gave up trying to wake him in the morning. But, dressed in his white linens and toting a heavy Army pistol, he still was on time for the roll call of the constabulary detachment.

"We're going to Palange," said the captain in com-

26

mand. "It's about thirteen miles. Do you think you can make it there and back?

Dick was already sweating profusely, but he stuck his chest out. "Yes, sir. Of course I can."

The detachment filed through the streets and out of the city, uphill and into the jungle. There the road narrowed into a trail barely wide enough for two men marching side by side. Dick had hoped that the trees would shade him from the hot sun; but the trail weaved, so that the relief was only sporadic. His eyes stung from perspiration that ran down the sides of his face in rivulets. The pistol seemed to weigh a ton. The loose webbing belt loaded with spare ammunition swung with every step, making the hard leather holster rub painfully against his right thigh. He hoisted the belt, taking in two extra notches, and marched on.

"Pace too fast?" the captain asked, smiling.

Dick was unable to utter a sound. He shook his head in the negative.

"We have to hurry," the captain explained. "We must get to Palange before the *ladrones* can alert the mayor there. We have orders to arrest him and bring him back for trial."

They entered a clearing. A burned house and two sun-bleached wooden crosses bore mute witness to the fierce insurrection in the not-so-distant past.

"Halt!" the captain commanded. "Five minutes' rest."

His words still echoed in the humid air when the sharp cracks of rifle fire from the thick underbrush sent the soldiers running for cover.

"Ambush! Return fire!"

Dick's tightened belt placed his holster too high. He

27

fumbled for his gun. The next thing he knew, the captain had knocked him off his feet. A dark object swooshed through the air and landed a yard away with a thud.

"A bolo knife." The captain motioned with his head. "Stay down. Watch for gun smoke in the brush, then aim at it and fire."

Bullets whistled overhead. Dick's heart hammered with a wild tattoo. Vainly he tried to remember what his book heroes had done under similar circumstances. His mind seemed to freeze on one thought—the unseen enemy was firing real bullets and he was a target, sprawled on the moist, hot ground.

Slowly he realized that in spite of the cannonade he was still very much alive. He lifted his head a trifle. There was a puff of blue smoke among the foliage . . . another and yet another. Since the enemy is under cover and we are not, Dick reasoned, I must try to find a better place—perhaps that charred wall.

He pulled up one knee, then the other. He began to crawl to the burned house.

"Get back, Dick!"

But Dick was almost there. Then, feeling safer behind the cover, he pulled out his Army pistol, rested it on a blackened timber, and fired at the next smoke he saw.

Suddenly the firing from the jungle ceased and the captain gave orders to resume the march. "Luckily we are between the *insurrectos* and our destination—they won't be able to warn the Palange mayor," he said. "And, judging by my experience, they won't bother us again."

They marched side by side in silence, until the captain spoke again. "You did well. Where did you learn to handle a pistol?"

"My father taught me."

"There was only one thing you did wrong," the captain said. "You crawled instead of making a sprint for that wall."

"Yes, sir. And thank you for saving me from that bolo."

The captain smiled. "Well, when you have men under your command, you'll do the same, I'm sure."

They reached Palange, arrested the unsuspecting mayor and brought him back to Manila. That night, October 9, 1902, tired as he was, Dick wrote a letter to his father:

"Today I went with a captain and some soldiers to a place called Palange, thirteen miles from here, where fighting has taken place, to capture a mayor who had stolen some money. We got the mayor and on the way back captured a Filipino spy, and as he was such a notorious spy and has done the Americans so much harm, he is going to be hung." . . .

In simple understatements Dick described his arrival, his welcome by Judge Adam Carson, and what he had seen of Manila and the surroundings. He wrote regularly from then on, reporting not only the immediate situation but the interesting bits of background he had learned in his travels throughout the Philippine Islands.

From Masbati he wrote on December 2: "During the Spanish-American War here, at one time they received news that Weyler, the Spanish general in Cuba, had invaded America and made a successful landing at Key West. Upon receiving this news, the Spanish governor here ordered a state fiesta or holiday and during the entire day church bells rang out furiously. You can imagine how taken aback they were when they received the news that their entire fleet was at the bottom of the sea, and that the first news was a lie sent out by their government to keep their spirits up. . . .

"We are waiting here for a boat to go to Samar, the place where fifty of our troops were massacred. I know you have read about it in the newspapers. There is still a good deal of fighting there now. Sam Carson [Judge Carson's relative] is there. . . . As soon as I get to Samar I will write Mother and tell her all about it."

Dick's calmness under fire during his first skirmish soon brought an official recognition, which he didn't mention in his letters home until much later. Endorsed with the governor's signature, the paper read:

Province of Sorsogon
Philippine Islands

Office of the Governor

TO WHOM THIS MAY COME—KNOW YE:
That I, the Governor and Sheriff of the Province of Sorsogon, in virtue of the authority vested in me by law 159 Article I, name as one of my deputy sheriffs, in this the chief city of my Province, Mr. Richard E. Byrd, Jr., native of the United States and at this moment residing in this, the capital of Sorsogon.

And so that this may take effect, he will take oath of office before Honorable A. C. Carson, Judge, which oath shall be attached to this paper.

Given in the government building of Sorsogon, October 22, 1902.

(signed)
B. MONREAL
Governor and Sheriff

Going on patrols, hunting monkeys and wild boar, Dick hardened. In a few months he could keep pace with the toughest of soldiers and he could aim his Smith service revolver as steadily as any U. S. Marine. He learned Spanish well enough to carry on a conversation and felt quite at home among the natives.

One day Judge Carson called Dick to his room. "I have some bad news which I expect you to take like a good soldier," he said. "The cholera is reaching epidemic proportions in the islands. While you have learned how to take care of yourself on patrol, this is a different kind of danger—something you cannot fight with your revolver or a rifle." He lighted a pipe and puffed on it thoughtfully. "You'll have to leave, I'm afraid."

"But how about you, Kit, and the others?"

"We have orders to stay."

Dick knew the Judge well enough not to argue, but the temptation was too great. He stood at attention. "Sir," he said, "I request permission to delay my departure for three days. I'd like to go on another hunt."

Judge Carson pulled an envelope out of his pocket. "Sorry, Dick. Your steamer sails tomorrow at the morning tide. Here are your tickets."

Dick tried to force down a warm lump in his throat. His eyes smarted as they had on that first march to Palange. He made a quick about-turn and stiffly marched to the door.

"Oh, incidentally, Dick," Judge Carson called after him, "I wasn't able to book you a passage directly to the States. I am afraid you'll have to travel by way of the Indian Ocean, the Red Sea, the Mediterranean, and the

31

Atlantic Ocean—all the way to Boston." He chuckled. "I hope you don't mind."

It took a couple of seconds for the fabulous itinerary to register. Then, forgetting his Army discipline, Dick rushed back and hugged the Judge. "Boy! That means I'll travel all the way around the world!"

Holding the boy at arm's length, the Judge said, "I thought this would soften the blow. No hard feelings then, eh?"

"No, *sir*!"

"In that case I'd better say good-bye now and wish you *bon voyage*," Judge Carson said. "I am holding court tomorrow and I won't be able to see you off. Give your parents my respects."

Back in his room, Dick began packing his suitcase hurriedly. All he could think of now was the endless expanse of ocean, the strange lands, and—even more strange—the excitement of being probably the first fourteen-year-old to circumnavigate the globe. Then he felt a battered piece of cardboard. He pulled it out—the itinerary tag his mother had tied around his coat button at the station in Winchester. He put it back, but when he was about to go to bed he fished it out again. He didn't quite know why he slipped it under his pillow.

Try as he would, Dick could not sleep. He got up, lit his oil lamp, opened the long envelope Judge Carson had handed him, and read the ports of call on the steamer ticket—Saigon, Singapore, Calcutta, Piraeus, Gibraltar, Boston.

BRONZED FROM THE LONG SEA VOYAGE, DICK BYRD leaned against the ship's rail as the Boston harbor tugs gently nuzzled the steamer into the wharf. Below, on the quayside, a throng of people milled impatiently, waiting for the gangplank to be fastened, waving their hats and handkerchiefs to the passengers on board.

Dick scanned the friendly upturned faces of strangers with mixed feelings. Yes, he was happy to get back. One more day and he would be in Winchester, telling Father, Mother, his brothers and friends about his adventures. Yet the still-fresh memories of the trip were like a powerful magnet drawing him back and filling him with strange nostalgia.

A wave of passengers carried Dick and his battered suitcase down the gangplank. He wriggled his way through the crowd and headed for the street. He was

33

about to hail a hack to take him to the South Station train when a group of newspaper reporters surrounded him, firing questions at him.

"Aren't you Dick Byrd, the globe-trotter and foreign correspondent for the Winchester *Star*?"

"I hear you were a guest of a maharaja."

"Is it true you saved a ship from sinking in a typhoon?"

"What was it like to capture a Filipino spy?"

Dick felt hot blood rush to his face. His first impulse was to run and hide; but a newspaper artist pushed himself to the fore, wet the pencil point in his mouth, and began to sketch. Attracted by the commotion, the curious passers-by ringed the reporters and Dick, cutting off all possible routes of escape.

Clutching his bag, Dick stammered his answers. No, he was not a maharaja's guest . . . he did not save the ship, nor did he capture a spy singlehanded. The reporters and crowd began to egg him on, but gradually Dick regained control of himself. He drew a deep breath. "I don't understand why you, gentlemen, should be so interested in me," he said calmly. "A lot of people travel every day. True, I am only fourteen but I'm quite capable of looking after myself. If you want stories for your papers, write about the U. S. Marines and our government officials in the Philippines who brave the *insurrectos* and a cholera epidemic. They are doing a truly heroic job there."

"All right, tell us about them," a reporter said.

"I'll be glad to. But I don't want to miss my train. If you would care to help me get to the South Station first . . ."

Later, when the train pulled out of Boston, Dick

quickly forgot his introduction to the press and his first taste of fame. His thoughts now sped 'way ahead, to Amherst Street.

They were all there—Father, Mother, Tom, and Harry —standing on the platform at Winchester, waving and cheering as Dick jumped off the train. The station building seemed different—smaller, somehow. But the fragrance of Mother's perfume had a comforting sameness and Father's hug was just as hard and firm as ever.

For the next few days Dick relived all his experiences, telling every detail of the trip at family meals and to visiting friends. Then the Byrd household began to settle down to making plans for the approaching school year.

For Dick it was going to be the Virginia Military Institute, the preparatory school modeled after West Point. Having tasted the military discipline and the Army life in the Philippines, Dick was sure this was what he wanted to do. He would become a soldier like Judge Carson used to be. Who knows, he might even be stationed in the Philippines or another faraway outpost.

Undersized for his age, Dick was the smallest in his class. But he compensated for his physical smallness by tenaciously training in athletics. While he took a merciless hazing from the upperclassmen, he devoted every spare moment to body-building exercises. Toughening his body and building his muscles became almost an obsession with him, but it paid high dividends. Soon, his steel grip and his top performance in all sports gained him the respect of his schoolmates.

One summer night in 1906 Dick was on guard duty. The campus was quiet except for the western breeze that swooshed through the tree branches in an erratic rhythm.

The mighty sound, now swelling, now subdued, brought back memories almost forgotten in the rigid, disciplined, busy life of Cadet Richard Evelyn Byrd, Jr. As he watched the swaying treetops, he could almost feel the roll and pitch of a ship's deck. He remembered the nights on the Pacific when the sky seemed to melt with the ocean into a deep-blue sphere sparkled with stars; the clairvoyance of navigation, the might of the ship's engines, the frail minuteness of the hull faced with the mountains of stormy waves . . .

Yes, the Army life would be fine, exciting perhaps, but still limited. That night Dick Byrd realized that what he really wanted was to travel and explore. He wanted the freedom only the seas could give him.

The next day Dick and his classmates discussed the importance of maps in military strategy. Spinning a large globe, one of the cadets said, "I wonder what an Army commander would do if he had to fight a campaign around the North Pole—why, the place is a blank on every map I've seen."

Another cadet chimed in, "Well, the Navy would have to get there first to bring the troops. I guess it would be up to the sailors to map the place anyway. Don't you think so, Dick?"

Dick nodded silently. Now the strange call of the sea he had heard the night before really made sense. With almost three-quarters of the globe covered by oceans, explorations by sea was obviously the thing. Take the North Pole, for example, he mused. One would have to at least approach it by sea. . . .

Inspired by these speculations, he wrote in his diary: "Someday I will reach and explore the North Pole." And his letters home began to carry broad hints of his recent change of heart.

Home on furlough, Dick presented his new plan to his father. "I've given the matter a great deal of thought, sir," he said. "With your permission I would like to go to Annapolis."

Mr. Byrd rubbed his chin thoughtfully. "Well, it will be some time before we could get you your appointment—"

"I've thought of that, Father," Dick said, grinning. "Couldn't I join Tom at the University of Virginia for a year?"

Mr. Byrd's eyes twinkled. "I see you have planned every move carefully."

"Yes, sir," Dick said with mock seriousness. "You have always said that a thorough plan is the best insurance for success."

"So I have, so I have." Mr. Byrd looked into his son's wide-open eyes. "Well, Dick, if this is *really* what you feel you must do, you have my blessings."

Dick stretched an inch as he braced himself to "attention" in the best V.M.I. tradition. "Thank you, Father," he said. Then he hugged him with all his might, almost knocking his father's glasses off in the process. "Thank you, thank you a million times. . . . Do you think I'll get the appointment?"

Mr. Byrd freed himself gently. "Anybody as determined as you are should never worry about anything," he said. "I'm sure you will get your appointment."

The appointment came through on May 28, 1908. The United States Naval Academy opened its gates to the new "plebe," Richard E. Byrd, Jr., who walked into the Yard wide-eyed with anticipation.

Eager to live up to the Academy's motto—*Ex Scientia Tridens* (From knowledge, sea power)—Midshipman Dick Byrd studied harder than ever before. And again being one of the smallest in his class, or a "sandblower," spurred Dick to an extra effort in body-building exercises and athletics.

He played tennis, wrestled, boxed, excelled in gymnastics, and made the second team in football. Before the plebe year was over, Dick became the captain of the second team and was elected chairman of the Athletic Committee.

In his second year at the Academy, Dick began to shine as a football star. He more than compensated for his light weight of 135 pounds with clear thinking, snap decisions, and bulldog tenacity.

That year it looked as though the midshipmen were about to lose to the Princeton Tigers. With only one minute left in the game, the score was 10 to 6 with the Tigers in the lead.

An excited shout exploded in the stands as Dick Byrd leaped up to intercept a Princeton pass. Pulling his chin in, he started the 48-yard run. The Tigers blocked, but he dodged out of trouble.

Cold autumn air burned in Dick's throat as he resumed his run. Thirty yards . . . twenty . . . ten . . . five . . . A step from the goal line, the Tiger defenders flung themselves at Dick in a last, desperate tackle.

TOUCHDOWN! The crowds in the stadium went berserk at this last-minute Annapolis victory.

Too late to stop their fierce impetus, the Tigers piled on top of Dick.

Later, when his teammates pried him loose, and helped him to his feet, he winced. "My leg . . ." His face was pale and drawn from pain, but he waved triumphantly as the middies carried him off the field.

Dick's right foot was broken in three places, and he spent the rest of the season rooting for his team. However, he recovered quickly and his fractures were almost forgotten in the excitement of preparations for the summer cruise to Europe.

The Academy cruise ship was steaming into the English Channel as the midshipmen made plans for their shore leave, with sight-seeing tours in London. But somehow Dick couldn't work up enthusiasm.

"What's the matter, Dick?" Midshipman Louis Denfield asked. "Aren't you looking forward to seeing the Tower of London, Buckingham Palace, the Guards, and the misty-eyed daughters of Albion?"

Dick covered his face. It was hot to the touch. "Take me to the sick bay, Lou," he said weakly. "I don't feel so good." That night he burned with typhoid fever. As soon as the ship made harbor, he was put ashore and taken to a Royal Navy hospital.

Dick fought his illness. The crisis passed and the slow convalescence began. All Dick could think of was the approaching football season and the big game against the Army. He reread the letter from the Academy coach, Captain Frank Berrian, especially one part: "Get well quickly. We shall need you here, especially since you are my choice for captain of the team."

Although still weak, Dick stubbornly crawled out of his hospital bed every night after "lights out." His eyes

39

smarted from sweat as he practiced push-ups and bends, exercising his muscles and toughening his body weakened by the long confinement.

He was about to leave the hospital when an orderly bounced into his ward waving a copy of the London *Times*. "Robert Peary discovered the North Pole," he said. "Here's the full story."

Dick didn't believe his ears. But there were the headlines and the long article. As he read on, he felt as though the world was collapsing around him. He envied that man Peary who had shattered his own most precious dreams of exploration.

"The man who never gives up," the newspaper writer called the polar explorer. Well, he, Midshipman Richard E. Byrd, Jr., was never going to give up, either. After all, there was still the South Pole.

Still gaunt and underweight after his four-month illness, Dick reported back at Annapolis in time for the fall training. He won the coveted position of quarterback and, that season, his team won an important game against Pennsylvania. The next opponent would be Army. But after the Pennsylvania game Dick collapsed from exertion and was rushed to the sick bay.

The doctor examined him and ordered a rest. "I'm afraid you'll have to give up football," he said.

"But, sir, how about Army?" Dick pleaded. "Couldn't I play just that one more game?"

The doctor folded his stethoscope. "Yes, I think you could. But a human body can take only so much. If you play the Army game, you will jeopardize your entire naval career. Would you take that risk?"

Dick's well-drawn mouth tightened as he jutted out his chin. He thought of the months of training and preparation for this big moment and the glory of a victory over the Army team. He was sure his team would win. . . . On the other hand, there was the Navy—the sea power and the power of exploration. "Sir," he said, "please let me break the news to the coach myself."

His football days behind, Dick turned to the less strenuous sports. He was a member of the rifle and pistol teams and he perfected his gymnastics until in his last year at Annapolis he was selected captain of the Navy's gym team.

That winter the team faced the intercollegiate championship of the year. To gain extra points and insure a victory, Dick devised an intricate stunt on the flying rings. At the end of a terrific swing, almost to the ceiling of the gym, he hoped to have enough time for a double somersault.

He meticulously calculated his every move, experimented and practiced until he was sure the stunt would work. Then came the day before the meet, with the gym packed with midshipmen. Their upturned heads followed Dick's pendular path. He swooped down, graceful as a sea gull diving for the waves, only to zoom up again. He swung higher and higher. Now . . .

The spectators held their breath. At the end of his upswing, Dick whirled. Once . . . again . . . He reached for the rings. His left hand connected—but his right grip missed. He fell.

A horrified cry went up from the crowd, then came a sickening thud as Dick crashed to the floor. Half-conscious from the shock, he tried to stand up but fell back in agonizing pain. His right foot and ankle were again fractured.

As Dick was taken to the hospital, telegraph wires all over the world flashed a message: ROALD AMUNDSEN REACHES SOUTH POLE.

4

DICK KNEW THE PAIN WOULD EASE IF HE ONLY COULD relax, yet he didn't dare try for fear of crying out. He bit his lips until he could taste the salty bitterness of blood. His eyes shut tight, he held onto the sides of his hospital bed.

Then he felt a cool touch on his burning forehead and heard a familiar, soothing voice. "Dick . . ."

He focused with great difficulty, as though waking from a nightmare. "Marie," he whispered.

Her lips quivered ever so slightly when she smiled at him. "Come on, lift your head a little," she said. "Let me fix your pillow. There. . . . Isn't that better?"

Under the magic of her nearness Dick's tense body slowly went limp and the pain receded. "Wonderful of you to come," he said.

Marie stroked his wavy hair. "Care to tell me what's troubling you?"

He winced. "The cast on my leg—"

"That's not what I mean," she said. "The doctor told me you were depressed. Whatever the cause, would you like to talk about it?"

Dick closed his eyes. As far back as he could remember Marie was always there. From the Tater Hill gang days in Winchester, over the years, she had listened, encouraged, and supported him in a way nobody else did. Not even Tom, Harry, or Mother had ever been able to share so fully in his troubles or triumphs.

And as she blossomed from a small, timid girl into a beautiful and poised young woman, their childhood friendship had matured into a mutual affection. It was like the merging of the ocean with the boundless air space on the horizon. Whether you stood still or traveled full steam ahead, the horizon was invariably there—sometimes hazy or even clouded over, but always mysterious in its calm, level beauty.

Dick looked at her. "It's a combination of things, Marie," he said in a low voice. "I've been advised to go back a class. I've already missed my mid-term exam and they don't think I can catch up in time for graduation. It's only six months away, you know."

"Do *you* think you can make it?"

Dick's blue-gray eyes hardened with determination. "Yes, but . . ." He turned his head away, then looked at her again. "Only you can understand, Marie. First it was Peary and the North Pole. Now Amundsen has explored the South Pole. There isn't anything worth-while to discover any more. Don't you see how pointless any struggle would be?"

Marie nodded with understanding. "Of course. It

wouldn't make any sense if this were really the case," she said evenly. "But one trip to the Pole is hardly an exploration—both Peary and Amundsen admitted that themselves." As she talked, her voice gained a note of conviction and her wide eyes radiated enthusiasm. "And how about the flying machines you wrote me about? Isn't flying in itself a virgin territory, waiting to be explored?"

Her enthusiasm was contagious. Dick propped himself on his elbow. A slight color livened his face. "Marie, you're wonderful. Even if there were nothing left to explore, you certainly are worth the fight. I'll fight, Marie, and I'll make it!"

The fractures, however, knitted very slowly. Two months after the accident, when Dick returned to the Academy, the bone on the side of his right ankle still was in two pieces. It clicked as he walked and sent hot stabs of pain with every step. But time was short, so Dick bore the pain without a limp or a wince. He studied day and night. He took the mid-term and the final examinations at the same time, and on June 8, 1912, Midshipman Byrd became Ensign Byrd, having graduated in the top half of his class.

On August 15, 1914, the *USS Washington* steamed into the shark-infested harbor of Puerto Plata, Santo Domingo, to take on a detachment of U. S. Marines from the transport *Hancock*. Dick Byrd, then a junior officer of the *Washington*, accompanied Commander Willard to the troop ship. They had just come aboard and Dick stood by the rail watching the launch dancing in the rough seas by the ship's side.

A wave struck the small boat's stern, knocking a sailor

overboard. Acting on impulse, Dick swung his leg over the rail and dived after the man.

As he plunged, Captain Louis Fagan, the skipper of the *Hancock*, raised the alarm. "Man overboard! Heave him a line!"

Before the life line snaked from the ship's deck, Dick was swimming toward the drowning sailor. He reached for the line, made it fast to the man and propelled him firmly toward the ship's side. Then he placed himself between the half-conscious sailor and the steel hull and cushioned the fierce buffeting of the seas until the man was hoisted on board.

Later Dick stood to attention as Captain Fagan reprimanded him for risking his life. "Losing one man would have been bad enough," Fagan said. "But we could have lost you, too, what with the sharks and the rough water. You could have drowned."

"Sir, I am sorry I caused you so much concern," Dick said. "But I wasn't really taking chances. I've been swimming since I was knee-high. Besides, that man was one of my crew and I, as an officer, was personally responsible for his life."

World War I had flared in Europe like a forest on fire when the *USS Washington* returned to the United States that fall. News bulletins told of the German "steamroller," the capture of Antwerp and the battle of Ypres. On the eastern front the Kaiser's armies had beaten the Russians at the bloody battle of Tannenberg.

Discussing world events with his fellow officers, Dick felt sure the United States would declare war on Germany and that the U. S. Navy would immediately go into action. "We can't let the French be slaughtered," he argued. "Wait and see, we'll be steaming for Europe before long."

However, the United States Congress did not share Dick's enthusiasm and the fleet stayed in home waters. Dick's next assignment was to the *Dolphin*—the yacht of the Secretary of the Navy, stationed in Washington, D.C.

At the farewell party on board the *USS Washington*, Dick's colleagues looked at him with envy. "You must have been born under a lucky star, Dick," one of them said. "Think of all those fabulous parties, the champagne and beautiful ladies. I'd give my eyeteeth for an assignment like that—the best in the Navy."

Dick smiled politely and shook hands. He hated parties and the empty glitter of social life. The only good thing about the new assignment was that he would be closer to home and to Boston, where Marie lived.

The first week after reporting on board the *Dolphin*, Dick caught a train to Boston. Marie met him at the South Station. "Your tropical tan is quite a contrast to our New England snow," she laughed. "Let's walk while you tell me all about your adventures in the Caribbean."

Happy to see her, Dick was bursting with special news. "Do you remember that day in the hospital?" he asked. "You said that flying needed exploring, or something like that. Well, I am an explorer—I've flown."

"How did it feel?"

His face radiant with the recollection, Dick said, "It's an experience one can never forget. There is the engine roar—quite deafening in spite of the leather helmet. The aircraft first bobs along the waves like a fast boat, then gradually the water hardens—the waves pound against the pontoon, make the aircraft shiver. Just as you think the machine is going to be pommeled to bits, the pounding ceases. You miss that nervous tremor. The sudden smoothness makes you feel motionless and sort of apprehensive until you look overboard."

"Was it fun to zoom up like a sea gull?"

"Well, the funny part of it is you don't have the sensation of climb. Instead, the ship and the hangars below seem to be sinking away from you. Soon they acquire a remoteness which makes them appear unreal. They are like little, fragile toys."

They walked toward the Commons hand in hand. Passers-by stared, some of them murmuring, "What a handsome couple!" But Dick neither saw nor heard anybody. His eyes veiled with a dream of his first flight, he kept talking.

"The clouds that look so distant from the ground are far more magnificent in their closeness up there. Yet there is something ominous about them. They are quite alive. You can see their cottony vapor in constant, swirling motion and you can feel their breath when you come near their puffed-up edges. They shake the aircraft with their currents as though to warn the aviator to steer clear—"

"Did it make you dizzy to come down for the landing?"

"Not at all, Marie. I suppose I was far too excited to feel anything except the disappointment that this magic of flight had not lasted longer."

Now they cut across the snow-covered Commons, away from the hustle of the busy city. "Dick, I have a feeling that you're preparing me for something," Marie said. "Just like that time in Winchester when you seemed so

48

excited about making peace with the Tater Hill boys, but all the while you knew you were going to the Philippines. And you saved the news until it was time to go home."

Dick chuckled. "I should know I can never keep anythink from you," he said, stopping. He took both her hands and held them firmly. "Marie, will you marry me?"

Her shapely mouth drew into a silent "oh" of surprise; the touch of pink on her cheeks darkened a shade. She lowered her head a trifle, and quickly looked up to meet Dick's eyes. "Of course I will. I said I would—a long time ago in Winchester. Remember?"

They were married on January 20, 1915. The wedding festivities lasted for three days and it seemed that all of Winchester celebrated with the Byrd family in one way or another.

Dick's happiness, however, was marred by his new transfer. Instead of an expected assignment to the fleet, he was transferred to the *Mayflower*—the Presidential yacht. While in Washington, Dick ran into Nathan Chase, his Academy classmate, who now flashed the lieutenant's (j.g.) insignia.

"Hello, Dick!" Chase slapped his friend on the shoulder. "Hey, what is this?" he said. "How come you haven't been promoted?"

Dick frowned. "I guess it's my bum leg. I can't stand watch aboard a real man-of-war—the yacht duty is about my speed now."

"Listen, I have an idea. You should transfer to Naval Aviation," Chase said. "You don't have to stand up to fly. Look at me—I've almost forgotten how to walk!"

Dick tried for a transfer again and again. Finally, discouraged by the polite refusals, he asked to be retired from the Navy. The orders retiring him on three-quarters pay came through on March 16, 1916. That day Dick recorded his heartache in his diary.

"Career ended," he wrote. "Not enough income to live on; ordered home for good. No chances of coming back; trained for a seafaring profession; temperamentally disinclined for business. A fizzle."

He closed his diary and put away the pen. The newspaper on his desk headlined the fierce battle of Verdun. His eye caught a sentence: "The French armies are on the verge of a total annihilation."

His muscular shoulders stooping, Dick stood over his desk. "Oh, God, what's wrong with me?" he whispered. "Is all my struggle to be for nothing?"

5

ABSENTLY DICK PICKED UP A COPY OF *Lucky Bag*, THE Annapolis magazine. He flipped through it until he found a page with his graduation picture on it. He read: "Richard Evelyn Byrd, Jr.—athlete, leader in all right things, friend and gentleman. Most of the time Dick wanders around with a far-away, dreaming look in his eyes and one wonders whether he knows whether he is coming or going. He is suffering from a malady that gets us sooner or later. He has already lived a life rich in experience and he will live a life richer still." . . .

What irony, Dick thought. Here he was in the prime of his life; only twenty-eight years old and already discarded by the Navy, in which he had put so many hopes.

"But he will always give to life more than he asks." . . . Dick snapped the magazine shut. What could he give to life—to anybody? What could he do, with his injured leg that held him back like a ball and chain?

Still holding the magazine, he slumped in his chair. The time-spanning magic of recollection took him to his father's library in Winchester. He remembered that day well. He had just taken a painful licking from huskier Tom. He had been a failure.

"Whether you are a failure or a success depends entirely upon you," Mr. Byrd, Sr., said. "We are only human and we all fail at times. But you must realize, Dick, that often a successful man is a long-time loser who tried again."

The vision vanished, but his father's words still reverberated in Dick's ears . . . "tried again." Well, he would try again. He slipped into his coat and strode from the house into the crisp spring evening.

For a week Dick exercised his body like a prize fighter before a championship match. True, the Navy would have been a short cut to exploration; but he would explore on his own. He would think of a way.

Humming a tune, Dick was going through his afternoon mail. There was a familiar long envelope from the Navy Department. He tore it open.

"Would you accept the post of inspector-instructor of the Naval Militia of Rhode Island?" the letter read. "You are hereby commissioned Lieutenant, junior grade, U.S.N. Your commission is retroactive, antedating your retirement by one day."

Dick waved the letter triumphantly. "Marie . . . how would you like to go to Providence, Rhode Island?"

She answered from the next room. "With you I'll go anywhere."

"Then let's pack."

Lieutenant Byrd worked like a dynamo. Within a few

months he organized the militia into a well-disciplined unit. The Governor of Rhode Island commissioned him Commander of the state's entire naval forces, and the Navy Department sent an official approval and a letter of commendation.

On April 6, 1917, the Providence newspaper boys electrified the city with their cries. "Extry, extry. . . . Congress declares war on Kaiser. . . . Read all about it!"

The next day Byrd was summoned to the Navy Department in Washington. Kissing Marie good-bye, he said excitedly, "Well, maybe I'm not such a cripple after all. I'll telephone you as soon as I know the name of my ship. . . . Or perhaps it will be an assignment to the flying school at Pensacola!"

The chief petty officer at the Navy Department saluted smartly. "Sir, you are to report to the Bureau of Personnel," he said.

"For an assignment?"

"Well, sir, that's your assignment. The office of the enlisted men's transfer under Commander Harry Shoemaker."

Day after day Byrd dutifully stamped papers and transferred men from one naval station to another. Time and time again he sent his requests through channels for his own transfer to the fleet. But the answer was always the same: "Sorry, you are medically unfit for sea duty."

When Byrd was beginning to give up hope, a transfer came—to another desk job as executive secretary of the Navy's Commission on Training Camps under Dr. Raymond B. Fosdick. Again Byrd started his barrage of requests for transfer, only this time he tried for Naval

Aviation. And, with Dr. Fosdick's approval, the Secretary of the Navy decided to let him go.

The monotony of the office work, the long hours of phyical inactivity, and the disappointments had taken a heavy toll of Byrd's health. His uniform hung on him like a hand-me-down from an older brother. His cheeks were hollow but his blue-gray eyes burned with fierce determination.

"Lieutenant Byrd," the president of the medical board said, "in my opinion the only recommendation this board can honestly make is to send you on an extended leave. To be blunt, your physical condition is appalling."

Byrd stood at attention. A tremor started in his legs and traveled upward until his chin began to tremble. He had come so close to the fulfillment of his dreams . . . he couldn't give up now. He wouldn't. He took a deep breath. Steady now, steady. He would have to convince the doctors somehow. . . .

"Sir, I realize the request I am about to make is somewhat unusual," Byrd said, forcing a casual tone of voice. "But the fact is that I want to fly more than anything else in the world. Therefore I ask a postponement of your decision for thirty days."

The medical officer nodded. "Seems reasonable."

Byrd continued. "But meanwhile I ask your permission to go to Pensacola and fly. If at the end of one month I show no physical improvement—"

"This is preposterous!"

But Byrd was now fighting. He pleaded and argued so convincingly that the board finally granted his request.

It was a hot and humid August morning when Lieutenant (j.g.) Byrd reported for duty at the Naval Aeronautic Station, Pensacola, Florida. Like a small boy, goggle-eyed at a fabulous Christmas present, Byrd watched the strange activity at the base. Mechanics maneuvering the flying boats on the concrete ramps; the confusion of the engines, some roaring at full throttle, others stammering rhythmically, idling and belching black smoke.

A shout from a crowd of grease monkeys attracted his attention. He followed their outstretched arms, pointing skyward to one of the aircraft.

It was a training plane—a mere speck against the deep blue sky. Its engine sputtered. The machine wobbled from side to side, hesitant and helpless. Then it dipped its blunt nose. Slowly at first, then faster, the machine plummeted to earth. The sound of its engine was like a desperate cry for help.

The crash tender responded with a blast of its alert horn. Stretcher bearers, medics, and drivers jumped on board and the boat squatted in its wake, pulling away at full speed.

The death song of the aircraft ended with a deafening crash. Out on the shallow bay a geyser of white spray bloomed. Concentric waves—dark messengers of disaster—ran from the spot to meet the speeding rescue boat. The alert horn was still wailing its shrill requiem for the doomed crew as the mechanics on shore resumed their daily tasks.

Byrd stood rooted to the spot.

"Hello, Dick!" A voice spoke from behind.

Byrd turned to face Nat Chase, his Academy classmate.

"Don't let that upset you," Nat said breezily. "We have two or three crashes a day."

They started walking toward a hangar, and Nat said, "Say, care to go with me?"

Still dazed, Byrd nodded. And before he could fully recover from the shock of the crash spectacle, a mechanic handed him a helmet and two wads of cotton wool.

"Stuff it in your ears," Nat said. "You'll need it up there."

They climbed into a flying boat. Nat opened the throttle and the surge of power pushed Byrd back against the seat. Out of the corner of his eye he saw the rescue boat hauling the limp bodies from the crash. Then the aircraft nosed upward and they were off and climbing.

Nat pointed to a gauge on the instrument panel. Its needle stood at four thousand feet. Nat made a nondescript gesture with his hand and, suddenly, the machine's left wing dipped.

Byrd grasped the sides of his bucket seat. The horizon went crazy. It lifted from the left. The sparkling water below slipped from under the plane like an immense rug—replacing the sky, which now hid under the plane's lower wings. Hanging against his safety belt, Byrd gasped.

As though touched by a magic wand, the blue bay kept going around until it swung below again. The powerful hand of gravity pushed Byrd back into his seat; but before he could regain his bearing, the nose of the plane pointed almost into the zenith and the engine's roar died down.

A crash?

Lazily the horizon tilted again. Like a giant platter whirling on a juggler's fingertip, the bay gyrated around the plane's nose. Byrd looked ahead, down the engine cowl. Framed in the shiny halo of a spinning propeller, there was the crash boat and the wreck. It came closer and closer—a focal point of the enormous vortex of motion. . . .

The motion stopped. The aircraft dived at the site of the crash as though pulled by a magnet. Then the crash boat disappeared from view. Byrd's head bowed to the might of the centrifugal force which now squashed him into the seat and veiled his vision with a gray mist. When he could see again, the engine droned merrily. Nat nonchalantly "essed" the plane, turning right and left like a figure skater after a command performance.

He nodded, motioning to Byrd to take over the controls.

Gingerly Dick's hand moved the control stick—left, right. The wings dipped accordingly, alert, obedient. He pulled back and made the horizon sink under the cowl. Gradually he felt a warm elation born of his new accomplishment of commanding the machine. Or was it the joy of conquering his own fears?

The crash? Somehow that was a part of the sea and the earth so far below and so remote. . . .

Nat took the controls again and swooped down for a landing. The stay wires of the wings sang their shrill, happy aria . . . the throttled-down engine popped and sputtered, displeased with the end of its freedom of the sky.

When they climbed out of the cockpit, Dick had forgotten the shock of the accident. His eyes shone with the reflection of the sky. "Thank you, Nat," he said.

Dick took the ground training and the flight instructions in his stride. Within six hours of flying, he soloed. As he climbed down after his first solo flight, he patted the fuselage like a veteran pilot.

"How did she go?" the mechanic asked.

"Couldn't have been sweeter," Dick said, and strolled nonchalantly toward the pilot's room.

Eight months later, on April 17, 1918, Byrd received his naval aviator's badge, number 608, and an assignment as a member of the Pensacola Crash Board—a group of experienced flyers whose job was to try to determine the causes of accidents.

Many of the accidents occurred on longer, cross-country flights. Several experienced pilots just vanished without a trace.

Byrd pondered this mystery and came up with a proposal. "I believe those inexplicable accidents happened because the pilots got lost," he said to the station's commandant. "My suggestion is, sir, that we put compasses in all airplanes."

"And what's wrong with following the landmarks, and map reading?"

"Nothing, sir," Dick said. "But suppose the visibility is bad, or you're over water and out of sight of land . . ."

The commandant scratched his head thoughtfully. "Well, you're right about the visibility. Go ahead—have the compasses installed. But as to flying far out to sea— why, I'm sure nobody has been foolish enough to try that."

While Byrd supervised the compass installation, the

commandant's words kept ringing in his ears. Here at last was a chance to do some air exploration, he mused; develop the airplane into a useful tool and put aviation in harness.

Multi-engined seaplanes had been arriving at Pensacola, and the Navy was building the largest flying boat yet—the NC–1. There was no reason why airplanes should be tethered to the landmarks. In fact, if one had enough fuel . . .

Byrd had to discuss his new idea with someone. Walt Hinton, of course—a fellow flyer who understood the potential of aircraft. Dick found Hinton in his room and at once unfolded his plan. "What do you think of organizing a flight across the Atlantic to Europe?" he asked.

Lieutenant Hinton extracted a cigarette from a pack; put it in his mouth, then took it out again. "Are you feeling all right, Dick? How would you fix your position in the middle of the ocean . . . plot your course? No siree, it can't be done."

Patiently Dick explained his plan. He had already started designing a driftmeter—a device which would accurately measure the side-sweeping motion of an aircraft caused by a cross wind. "And what do you say we try to get a sun fix with a good old Navy sextant?"

By the end of his next cigarette Hinton agreed that Byrd's idea was not so crazy after all. The following day the two pilots took off on a long flight far out to sea.

However, the Navy standard sextant did not work unless the airplane flew practically at sea level and unless the horizon was unobscured by clouds or haze. Back in his room, Byrd sat at his desk and drew. The horizon line was absolutely necessary to establish the elevation of the sun or a star. He remembered his voyage to the Philippines . . . and Mr. MacDonald, the first mate of the SS Sumner. Yes, the horizon was needed to establish a level plane—a level!

He rushed out of his room. "Walt! I've got it! Look!" Byrd burst into his friend's quarters and feverishly sketched his idea. "All we have to do is use a modified level—an air bubble," he said. "When the bubble is in the middle the sextant is level, no matter how high you fly and how obscured the horizon. Don't you see?"

"Dick, this is stupendous!" Walt punched his open palm. "Let's get a couple of mechanics—build the darned thing at once."

The bubble sextant worked like a dream. Byrd and Hinton flew to the limit of their plane's range and navigated back, making a landfall smack over Pensacola.

Now Byrd wrote to Walter Camp, an influential friend of the family: "I am very anxious to attempt the hydro-aeroplane flight of the Atlantic and, thinking of all my acquaintances who might be able to help me in putting this through, I have decided that you are about the only one who could fill the bill. . . .

"My plan would be to use one of the new, big flying boats. . . . These seaplanes will have three Liberty motors and will, I think, have sufficient fuel capacity for a trip to the Azores. From the Azores, it is only eight hundred miles to England.

"This is quite an undertaking and will need considerable preparation. I will take a crew of five men and we will all train according to plans laid down by you. . . ."

Three days later Byrd received a very encouraging telegram from Walter Camp. Apparently Camp had told Admiral Peary about Dick's plan and they both had gone to the Navy Department urging that such a flight be undertaken.

6

THE NAVY DEPARTMENT HUMMED WITH WARTIME AC-
tivities. Reservists, in too-tight uniforms, and young volunteers mingled with the service-wise regulars, all
anxious to go "over there"—to Europe.

Byrd impatiently went from office to office, but nobody
seemed to know about the projected transatlantic flight.
Finally, on August 12, he found a young lieutenant who
vaguely recognized his name.

"Byrd . . . Byrd . . . ah, yes." He rummaged in a pile
of papers. "Here are your orders."

Oblivious of the crowd, Byrd opened the envelope and
read. He was promoted to Lieutenant Commander. A
good beginning, he mused. Then: "You are to proceed
to Halifax, Nova Scotia, Canada . . . to establish two air
naval bases there . . . the aircraft under your command
shall patrol the coastal waters for enemy submarines. . . ."

Not even a mention of the big flight. Nothing. He leaned against the wall. If it had been an order to go overseas he wouldn't have minded, but this—this exile where he would be as useful as a second man in a single-seater plane . . . Bitterness and disappointment welled up in him. He stuffed the orders into his pocket and stormed the Bureau of Personnel.

He argued, pounded desks, and pleaded. But the orders had been cut and there was no way to change them. Resigned, Byrd returned to his hotel.

"Something for you, sir." The desk clerk handed him an envelope.

Another set of orders.

From: Chief of Naval Operations
To: Commanding Officer, Naval Air Station, Halifax
Subject: Refueling Station in Newfoundland—proposed establishment of

1. It is desired to locate a suitable rest and refueling station on the east coat of Newfoundland.
2. The general requirements for this station are:
    a) sufficient area of sheltered water for maneuvering of large flying boat type seaplane with full load,
    b) sufficient depth of water for a destroyer or seagoing tug,
    c) telegraph or long distance radio is highly desirable.

This was it! His transatlantic flight was going off after all! He read further:

. . . Inasmuch as large seaplanes will probably not be supplied to air stations in Canada before the next spring,

63

the proposed station will not be established until that time, but the inspection should be made as soon as practicable without due interference with your present duties.

(signed)   W. S. BENSON

That last paragraph dampened Byrd's spirits a little. But he immediately sent a telegram to Walt Hinton: SITUATION PROMISING. AM GETTING YOUR ORDERS THROUGH TO JOIN ME IN HALIFAX. DICK.

Two weeks later Byrd greeted his friend Hinton at the newly established U. S. Naval Air Station across the bay from Halifax harbor. "This isn't much," he said, pointing to the tents and the crews working on the landing ramp. "But it's something."

They walked past the row of small seaplanes. A chief petty officer saluted smartly. "Sir, we'll be ready for the first patrol tomorrow morning, except that we haven't got any bombs."

"I've already attended to that," Byrd said. "The Canadians are letting us have some of their depth charges. We'll sling them under our fuselages. Assign ten men to that detail. I'll supervise the loading myself."

The next day, praying, Byrd took off on the first patrol. The depth charges were ticklish weapons—certainly not suited for air delivery. But following their commanding officer's example, the detachment carried out daily missions without mishap.

Proper bombs came, but no enemy submarines were sighted. Byrd and Hinton found a good base for the big NC planes at Trepassey and conducted thorough preparations for the transatlantic flight. Byrd perfected his bubble sextant and his driftmeter. He plotted courses to

Europe, calculated fuel consumption, and planned every detail.

"We'll make it, Walt," he said. "Just think of the boost to our troops' morale when we land our giant NC plane over there in a matter of hours after the take-off."

But hours, days, and weeks dragged without word from Washington. Then came November 11, 1918, and the Armistice. In the midst of jubilation a mailman brought orders. Byrd was to turn the air station over to the Canadians and return home at once.

In spite of the influenza epidemic, which was taking a heavy toll, Washington, D.C. was wild with excitement and victory parades when Dick made his way to the Navy Department.

Captain N. E. Irwin, the Director of Aviation, was out of the office, but Lieutenant Kirkpatrick greeted Byrd with elation. "Well, Dick, the big flight is coming off," he said. "Commander J. H. Towers is running the operation."

Byrd could hardly contain himself. "Hurray for good old Navy! Am I glad I haven't unpacked! I suppose we'll start at once . . ."

Kirkpatrick fiddled with a paper clip. "Take it easy, old man. I'm afraid you don't understand. Here, read this."

Byrd's mouth slowly fell open as he read the directive. "No officer or man who has had foreign duty will be permitted to be a member of the transatlantic flight expedition. This includes those who have been on Canadian detail."

He dropped the paper on the desk. "They can't do this to me," he murmured. "I've planned everything—"

"I am terribly sorry. But you know old man Irwin. He says he wants you at Pensacola."

"Pensacola?" Byrd shouted. "I've had enough shunting, being pushed aside. I'm going to see Irwin!"

The room spun around, and Byrd, out of balance, groped for a chair. Alarmed, Kirkpatrick summoned an ambulance. The intern's verdict was influenza.

Two weeks of fighting for his life in a naval hospital left Byrd weak but still burning with disappointment. As soon as he was well enough to walk, he demanded his uniform and forced the orderlies to help him dress.

Pale and shaky, Byrd reported to Captain Irwin. "I demand a revision of my orders, sir," he said, his voice trembling.

Built like a prize fighter, Irwin towered over Byrd. "Why, Commander?"

Byrd gave vent to his bitterness. "Because I've lived this project. I've laid every inch of the course; calculated every ounce of load, every drop of fuel. I've designed and tested new instruments. If I am sent to Pensacola now, you will be guilty of waste of man power . . . mismanagement of naval personnel."

Realizing he was speaking to a superior officer, Byrd halted abruptly.

"Well?" Irwin said. "Anything else?"

"That's about the size of it, sir."

Irwin smiled. "I'd heard rumors that nobody wins against you. I guess I am no exception," he said. "All right, consider your orders canceled. Report to Commander Towers—Transatlantic Flight Section of the Bureau of Aeronautics."

Victory at last! Byrd rushed to the telephone to share

66

his triumph with Marie. "I think this is the end of my bad-luck streak, darling," he said. "By making this flight I'll be able to prove that aviation is not only a weapon of war . . . perhaps they will let me fly to the North Pole."

"It's wonderful. Dick, and I'm so happy for you," Marie said. "But I do think you should come home for a rest. Can you?"

"I wish I could," Byrd said. "Perhaps I can make it for a long week end. There's so much to do."

Marie's voice was steady and loving, as always. "I understand. I'll be waiting."

By April, 1919, the Transatlantic Section set up a base of operations at Rockaway Naval Air Station, Long Island, New York. Three giant NC flying machines were delivered and Byrd busied himself training crews in navigation. On May 8, at 10:00 A.M., the three flying boats, their engines at wide-open throttles, thundered into the wind in a formation take-off.

NC–3, the lead plane, gathered speed to the mighty chorus of four Liberty engines. Sharp feathers of spray darted from under the plane's nose as Commander Towers pulled back on the control yoke. In the copilot's seat Byrd felt the quickened thumps of the waves against the hull. Like impatient heart beats they accelerated, then stopped—in awe of the magic of flight.

NC–3 was airborne. NC–1 and NC–4 followed like enormous prehistoric birds, edging closer to the leader as they set course for Newfoundland—into the unknown.

The crescent of Cape Cod slid under the NC–3's nose and vanished astern. Now, out of sight of land, the navi-

67

gation was up to Byrd. He checked the position, course, speed—ever listening to the engines.

Radio messages crackled in Byrd's headset. "NC–4 to NC–3—engine trouble. Will have to land."

The two remaining planes droned on and at 7:00 P.M. Byrd sighted Halifax harbor. "Right on the nose," he wrote on a pad and passed the message to Towers.

After a well-deserved rest and a thorough check of the planes, the formation again took off and headed for Trepassey, Newfoundland.

Five thousand feet. Below, white shapes like a huge fleet of sailboats dotted the dirty-green sea. Byrd reached for his binoculars. Icebergs! As he watched the parade of the arctic messengers, he noticed a change in the wave patterns. The wind must have shifted suddenly.

His drift indicator confirmed the shift. "Change course 15 degrees right," Byrd wrote on the pad.

Towers scribbled back. "If your gadget is wrong, we'll wind up in mid-ocean—out of gas."

Byrd took another sighting and confirmed the new course.

Towers shrugged, as though to say, "It's your funeral." But he changed the course.

Byrd scanned the misty horizon. No trace of land. What if his drift indicator had been wrong? A hot wave of doubt welled in him. He dropped a smoke bomb overboard. It landed and pointed the wind direction with its thin plume of smoke. Bent over his drift indicator, Byrd sighted on the smoke through the parallel wires—noting the angle. Still 15 degrees.

The mist shrank the field of vision to a hazy circle directly below the plane. Byrd glanced at his chronometer. They should be making landfall at Trepassey within one minute.

Seconds dragged. Suddenly a powerful updraft slammed the machine from below. Byrd bent in his seat under the force. The next gust stopped the ascent as though the ballooning machine had hit an invisible ceiling. Byrd's helmeted head struck the top of the cabin. But his pain vanished as Towers passed him a scribbled note. "Land below—Trepassey—you did it again!"

At Trepassey the two NC's were again checked by crews of mechanics. Later the NC–4 rejoined the company in time for a formation take-off on the first-in-history transatlantic flight.

"Dick, you just have to come along," Towers said. "If ever we needed your navigation sleight of hand, it's on this fifteen-hundred-mile hop over water."

"Well, I'm ready and more than willing," Byrd said. "I've waited months for this chance."

But that night Byrd received a brief message from Washington: YOU ARE NOT, REPEAT NOT TO ACCOMPANY TOWERS ACROSS TO EUROPE. IRWIN, CAPT. U.S.N.

On May 16, Byrd climbed a hill overlooking the harbor. He watched the three planes take off. As the machines picked up speed, Byrd unconsciously grew tense. The breeze dulled the engine roar, yet he listened attentively—his hand poised to nurse the throttles, perhaps cut the magneto switches in case of trouble.

The formation headed east and slowly melted into the blue haze on the horizon. Only then did Byrd realize that he had been gripping two clumps of grass. He opened his hands and let the breeze carry the torn stalks away.

7

BY THE TIME BYRD REACHED WASHINGTON, THE TRANS-atlantic flight had already made headlines. The NC–4 had landed in Lisbon, Portugal. The other two planes, although disabled, reached Ponta Delgada harbor in the Azores. But in the wake of the news came editorial comments whch only added to Byrd's feeling of defeat.

Aviation had passed its peak, the writers maintained. The precarious Atlantic crossing by air had proved that the man in the street would never risk flying. Aviation did have a future, but only as a sport—a dangerous pastime for a few daredevils.

Seeking refuge from the hostile atmosphere of Washington, Byrd went to Winchester. But his brothers and his father shared the popular opinion.

"I think you should turn to something more worth-while, especially now that you have your son to take care of," Mr. Byrd said. "Flying is certainly not for a mature man your age."

"I'm sorry to disagree, Father. But I see aviation as a universal way to travel—a powerful tool of exploration. True, flying is not safe yet; but it can be made safe and it will be. All we have to do is work at it—develop better aircraft—"

"And break your neck in the process," Mr. Byrd cut in.

"I have to die anyway, Father. And I'd rather die for the cause I believe in."

That evening Dick paced the darkening streets of Winchester. He breathed the spring air deeply, rhythmically, savoring the familiar fragrance of the apple blossoms. Maybe Father was right, he thought. Maybe he should settle down—leave the Navy and get into the apple-growing business. Certainly he wasn't meant to be an explorer. What had he accomplished for all his struggle, what had he to show for it? A string of miserable failures . . .

Deep in his thoughts, he turned the corner and bumped into a tall man. "I beg your pardon," he said, not even looking at the stranger.

The man took a step back. "Dick! Ah . . . I mean . . . Commander!"

Byrd looked up. The familiar voice—the huge, bony frame. "Jake?"

Jake's big white teeth flashed in the dark. "Sure, it's me. Golly—you remember me after all these years."

The two men shook hands—Jake pumping hard and Byrd unconsciously flexing his muscles, gripping Jake's hand as hard as he could.

"Been reading about you in the paper," Jake said

sheepishly. "The time you pulled a sailor out of the sea, the medals you got and how you been flying in them machines, and about your kid—Dickie." He gave a chuckle of embarrassment. "You going someplace—I mean someplace in particular?"

"No, Jake," Byrd said. "Just walking."

"I'll walk with you a piece. Golly—wait till I tell the missus about this."

As they fell in step, Byrd recognized the street. He had wandered up Tater Hill. He remembered the fierce battles and the last encounter with the gang.

"Remember?" Jake pointed to a vacant lot.

They both laughed, Jake a little nervously and Byrd with sudden relief.

"How could I forget?" Byrd said. "That day you gave me the biggest scare of my life."

"Oh, go on—you ain't the scary kind, flying and all that." Jake shook his head vigorously. "No siree. Like I was telling the boys—if Dick Byrd sets his mind to something, I said, he don't quit until he gets it. He ain't afeared of nothing!"

The simple and sincere accolade made Byrd blush. He felt the warmth creeping up his face and he was grateful for the darkness. "I haven't been doing so well," he said.

"Been hurt again?"

"No."

Jake was expectantly silent.

Byrd was trying to find a way to explain his situation. Somehow he wanted to hear Jake's opinion. Softly at first, then louder, like an engine revving up for take-off, he told about flying and his vision of air travel and exploration. "The trouble is, people don't see it my way," he said.

Evidently mulling over the revelation, Jake was quiet except for an occasional "Hm."

They reached the corner of Braddock and James, and Jake stopped. "And you think them machines will be flyin' to the end of the world and back someday? You think they'll do us some good?"

"I do, Jake."

"Well, I ain't much of a thinking man. But if you're sure we ought to have them . . . ah . . . airplanes, then I'm for it. And let me tell you this, Dick—everybody will back you, everybody in Winchester; well, leastways on Tater Hill." He took Byrd's hand and pumped it again. "I live down the street—I got to go now."

"So long, Jake. It's been good talking with you."

" 'Bye, Dick," Jake chuckled. "Wait till I tell my missus!"

Byrd almost ran all the way back to Amherst Street. He thudded up the wooden porch and collided with his brother Tom. They grappled playfully.

"Hey, what got into you, Dick?"

"Nothing new," Byrd laughed. "I'm going to fly across the Atlantic if I have to flap my own wings!"

Back in Washington, Byrd landed in the midst of a fierce political battle on Capitol Hill. General Billy Mitchell was leading a fight not only for aviation but for air power. Under the bombs dropped from aircraft, the German submarine *U–117* went down. Then another war trophy, the German cruiser *Frankfurt*, was bombed from the air and later the battleship *Ostfriesland* was sunk by Billy Mitchell's bombers.

Although still loyal to the Navy, Byrd was basically in agreement with Mitchell's ideas. In fact, it was Byrd's own campaign that gave the Navy its Bureau of Aeronautics. Still, while the battle for air power was on, Byrd had no time to plan his air exploration. And it was not until the summer of 1921 that he was able to propose his nonstop flight across the Atlantic.

Theodore Roosevelt, Acting Secretary of the Navy, called Byrd into his office. "Why don't you wait until the Navy develops an airplane that can make a nonstop flight from New York to Europe?" he asked. "The JL plane you're proposing to fly is far too unreliable for such a long flight. We don't want to lose you, Byrd—we need your services in the Navy."

Byrd argued, but Roosevelt was firm in his decision and the permission for the flight was denied.

Just then, the U. S. Navy had bought a dirigible in England—the ZR-2, which was to fly across the Atlantic to the United States. Immediately Byrd requested to be put in charge of navigation on the trip.

Admiral W. A. Moffett, the Chief of the newly established Bureau of Aeronautics, listened to Byrd's request, then smiled. "It's just the job for you," he said. "Commander Louis Maxfield, in charge of the airship, is a splendid officer, but the ZR-2 is a fifteen-million-dollar investment. With you to navigate the airship I'll be able to sleep nights—I'll know the ship will arrive here safely. Say hello to all our friends in London—have a good trip."

Byrd reached London on August 20, 1921—two days before the trial flight of the ZR-2 at Howden. He telephoned Commander Maxfield at once. "Could you put me down on the list of those to go on the trial flight?" he asked.

"Only if you come down here right away and report in person," Maxfield replied. "It's a big event—we have a long waiting list, so hurry. If you catch the afternoon train, you'll just make it."

On the way to the station Byrd's taxi was held up in traffic and he missed the train. When he finally arrived at Howden, the crew and passenger list was closed.

"Sorry, Dick," Commander Maxfield said. "But if you take the train to Pulham, you can join us there. So long, Dick!"

Byrd was among the spectators when the seven-hundred-foot airship cast off her mooring lines and majestically rose into the air. Her engines humming, she slowly sailed away.

Again he didn't quite make it. Byrd thought of the NC transatlantic flight a few years before. Would he ever be able to cross the Atlantic by air? Would any of his exploration dreams ever come true? Failure after failure, he mused. To run to pattern, he would probably miss train connections and arrive at Pulham in time to wave the ZR–2 off. . . .

Changing trains in London the next day, Byrd heard the newsboys' cries: "Extra! Extra! Big airship crash near Hull! Paper, sir?"

The account of the crash was brief, but there was no mistake—the ZR–2 had gone down in flames, only a few hours after he had seen it take off.

Byrd was on the next train for Hull. When he arrived on the scene of the disaster, Royal Navy crews were still pulling bodies out of the Humber River. Out of the forty-nine crew members of the ZR–2, only five survived.

The wreckage, partially covered by water, lay in the middle of the river. In the gloom of the foggy morning, curious spectators milled aimlessly on the river bank, pointing, shaking their heads, and murmuring.

" 'Tis God's way to show that man is not meant to fly," said a stranger.

Byrd heard the remark, but he was still too shaken to reply. He remembered it a few days later when he stood on the rolling deck of the battleship *Olympia* headed for the States. The ship was bringing home the body of the Unknown Soldier.

If men died in air crashes because God didn't want people to fly, Byrd thought, was the death of the Unknown Soldier, of the thousands who lost their lives in the war, a sign that men were not meant to fight for freedom? Or was it merely the price of struggle for a better world?

Flight certainly could bring the world's nations closer together . . . promote peace. Therefore, flight as an instrument of progress was worth the supreme sacrifice, Byrd reasoned with himself. Maxfield and the rest of the ZR–2 crew gave their lives for the cause they believed in. And it was up to those still flying to see to it that the sacrifice of their fellow pioneers had not been in vain.

8

REPORTING BACK FOR DUTY IN WASHINGTON, BYRD HAD a plan mapped out. He would resign his commission and organize air exploration on his own. "When Amundsen explored the polar regions, I was too young to do anything about it," he said to Admiral Moffett. "Well, I am not too young now and I hear Amundsen is planning to fly to the North Pole. I have to do something about it." He handed over his resignation letter.

"I understand how you feel, Dick," Moffett said. "But I wish you wouldn't resign just yet. You know the feelings about aviation on Capitol Hill—very little understanding of our problems and even smaller appropriations. We need you to help the Navy do something about it."

Byrd looked his superior squarely in the eye. "You are putting me in a very difficult position, Admiral," he

77

said. "You know how I feel about exploration and you also know where my loyalties lie."

"Yes, I do." Moffett looked away. "I thought you might have trouble deciding. I . . . ah . . . believe it might make it easier if I didn't accept your resignation." He handed the letter to Byrd. "Of course you can go over my head."

Byrd drew down his eyebrows. "Very well, I am staying. And here's something we should do at once—establish Naval Aviation reserve stations in the country to train personnel, men we need to carry on the fight for aviation."

"Excellent idea," Moffett said. "But what do you propose to use for money?"

"Well, let's organize the stations without the money."

"All right, Dick—you do it."

Armed with orders, Byrd rounded up veteran naval aviators in Massachusetts and presented his plan of action. "Beg, borrow, or—well, requisition," he told them. "But we've got to get a station going as soon as possible."

Within a few months the Massachusetts flyers had their Naval Air Station at Squantum, Boston. They rebuilt an old seaplane and started training reserve crews.

While traveling from city to city on his mission, Byrd kept an eye on the news about Amundsen. The Norwegian explorer was now in the States, raising funds for his polar air expedition. With the backing of Lincoln Ellsworth, a New York financier, Amundsen bought two Dornier-Wal planes and set the date of his flight—May 21, 1925.

The only thing to do, Byrd decided, was to speed up the organization of the naval reserve—wind up the project in time to start a polar air expedition of his own. Putting in twenty-hour days, Byrd set up air stations in New York and Chicago. He rallied naval aviators on the west coast and got back to Washington to plead for funds before the Naval Affairs Congressional Committee.

Seeing so many reserve stations already in operation, Congress appropriated funds to continue the naval air reserve training. And Byrd again turned his mind to air exploration.

At that time Commander Donald B. MacMillan was planning an expedition to western Greenland. His letter to the Navy Department said that he planned to do some flying and would like to borrow an amphibious aircraft from the government.

Admiral Moffett immediately summoned Byrd. "Why don't you join forces with MacMillan?" he said. "He already has his schooner *Bowdoin* and the small steamer *Peary*; also he is experienced in operating in the Arctic."

"But I have already started planning my own expedition," Byrd said. "Edsel Ford and John D. Rockefeller, Jr., have given me fifteen thousand each; Bob Bartlett raised an additional ten thousand—"

"You'll need that money for equipment, food, and so on," Moffett argued. "But if you go with MacMillan, the Navy will supply you with three NA planes and pilots—the best we have. Also we shall make you the commander of the Naval Aviation Unit for that expedition. What do you say?"

Byrd calculated quickly. "You're right. It will save me transporting our aircraft to Greenland—"

"Of course," Moffett said. "Once you establish your base in Etah, you'll be able to explore by air on your own.

79

And think of the boost you'd give Naval Aviation if you did locate that mysterious polar land Admiral Peary mentioned in his reports."

"Well, I'm game," Byrd said. "Just one more thing—I'd like to take along a crew of topnotch mechanics."

"Fine," Moffett said, opening a folder. "Here are the names: Bennett, Floyd, Chief Machinist Mate—excellent record as an aviation mechanic, and he's a pilot too." ... They went over the list. "I'll have orders cut at once for Lieutenant Schur and Chief Warrant Officer Reber as your relief pilots," Moffett said. "Bennett and the rest of the mechanics too."

"One more thing, Admiral. Speed is of the essence. If the conditions up North are right, I would like to try flying to the Pole—and I'd hate to find that Amundsen and Ellsworth had beaten us to it."

Commander Byrd's Boston home at 9 Brimmer Street became the headquarters of the newly born Naval Aviation Unit. Working virtually around the clock, Byrd often spent entire nights in his study on calculations and plans—to the smallest detail.

He concentrated on his work so hard that he didn't hear or see his brother Tom enter the study one evening.

"Hi, Dick! Come back to earth and stay awhile," Tom said, laughing.

Getting no answer from his preoccupied brother, Tom made his way among the charts and papers and stood behind his brother's chair. Still chuckling, he lifted the would-be explorer from the desk—chair and all.

Shaken from his work-trance and recognizing the intruder, Commander Byrd shouted mockingly, "Let me down, you big bruiser! Have you no respect for your older brother, the father of four?"

Tom put him down and the two men clasped hands.

"Well, well, well . . . How are you, Papa?" Tom said, smiling broadly. "I've seen Marie on my way in. But how are the kids?"

"Just fine, Tom. Little Richard Evelyn Byrd the Third is quite a boy, and as for the girls—Evelyn is almost catching up with Dickie to the distress of Katherine, who, incidentally, has started to talk since you saw her last. You'll see them all tomorrow."

Tom shook his head. "Don't think I will. I'll be catching an early train for New York. I'm a businessman now —have to work hard."

Byrd slapped his knees. "Of course! I almost forgot Harry talked you into that apple-growing deal."

"It's quite a deal—big business."

"With you and Harry in it, I'm sure it is. Say, how is Harry?"

Tom folded his powerful frame into a leather chair. "Brother Harry? He's been doing so well with his balanced-budget battle cry in the State Senate that he may become next governor of the Commonwealth of Virginia."

They chatted late into the night before Tom stood up, ready to go. "Ready for bed, Dick?"

"No, Tom. But you go ahead. I still have a few things to do before morning. I'm trying to wind up the preparations so that the expedition can sail sometime next month."

However, preparations took longer than Byrd had anticipated. By March, 1925, he knew his expedition wouldn't be able to sail in time to compete with Amundsen.

On May 21 Amundsen's flight took off from Kings Bay, Spitsbergen, as scheduled, the newspapers reported. Byrd took the news calmly. But a week passed without word from the Norwegian explorer—obviously his aircraft had been forced down somewhere in the arctic wilderness.

Byrd called a conference. "We must speed up our preparations as far as safety permits," he told MacMillan. "I believe our goal now should be the search and rescue of our Norwegian colleagues."

Three weeks later the *Bowdoin* sailed out of the Navy Yard at Boston, Massachusetts. The steamer *Peary*, with Byrd's aviation unit on board, followed in the schooner's wake. However, by the time the two ships put into Wiscasset, Maine, news came from Europe that Amundsen and Ellsworth had safely returned to Spitsbergen. Apparently they had underestimated fuel consumption for their planes and were forced down short of their destination.

Byrd and his crew held a double celebration. Toasting Amundsen in hot cocoa, Byrd said, "Here's to the great explorer's rescue—may he live long to give us another race someday."

"And here's to Amundsen for giving us another chance to be the first to fly to the Pole," Bennett said, lifting his cup.

Under the expert command of MacMillan the two ships plowed north. Imperceptibly the sea breeze chilled until one day the lookout on the *Peary* shouted a warning: "Berg-ho!"

Byrd and Bennett climbed on deck. Off the starboard bow, away on the horizon, there was a white speck glistening in the cold rays of the northern sun. As the ship drove on, the speck grew into an iceberg—a lofty castle atop a mountain of glass. Then it swerved in the current —to become a ghostly giant with outstretched arms, barring the ship's path.

Another berg materialized as though summoned by the first. Then more and more appeared until the horizon became a rampart that opened mysteriously in ever-narrowing passages to lure the fragile ships into the emerald labyrinth of arctic waters.

"Gee," Bennett said softly, "I never imagined the North was like this. It's almost like flying among the clouds on a sunny day."

Reluctantly Byrd turned from the parading bergs. Bennett's eyes, widened in awe, shone with the pale blue of the sky. "Gee . . ." he repeated.

The young man's reverence was like an echo of Byrd's own. "Would you like to fly to the Pole with me, Bennett?" he said.

Bennett gasped in surprise. "The Pole—sure, Commander. You mean from Etah?"

"Well, not directly," Byrd said, smiling at Bennett's alacrity. "We'll have to look for Crocker Land first. But God willing, and weather permitting, we might make a dash for the Pole." He explained how they would establish an advanced air base at the northern edge of Ellesmere Island. From there they would explore the Arctic Sea—follow Peary's vague directions and try to locate the land he had seen on his polar trek.

"Commander, I'm not much of a planner," Bennett

said. "But when it comes to babying the engines on the ground or in the air—well, I guess I might come in handy."

On the first of August the *Peary* followed the *Bowdoin* into Etah harbor. The Loening amphibian planes were uncrated and reassembled. Bennett and his mechanics worked under the midnight sun—tuning up the engines, tightening the bracing wires of the NA biplanes, and checking every detail.

Byrd was everywhere. He helped his mechanics load the planes with extra gasoline, food, and emergency equipment—including Byrd's pride and joy, the inflatable dinghy he had designed himself. And three days later the aviation unit was ready for the base-laying flights to Ellesmere Island.

However, the capricious arctic weather held the planes down for four more days. Gales battered the three anchored planes, and drifting bergs had to be constantly fended off lest they smash the thin metal floats.

Finally, at 9:00 P.M. on August 8 Byrd took off in the NA–3. Then Lieutenant Schur, with Commander Mac-Millan as passenger, roared into the air in the NA–2, following in the prop wash of Byrd's plane.

Steering by the sun compass especially developed for arctic flights by Albert Bumstead of the National Geographic Society, Byrd set course for Ellesmere Island.

Ice-packed Smith Sound slid under the plane's hull, then Cape Sabine and Knud Peninsula, poking its dark rugged peaks through the woolly blanket of clouds.

Byrd, crouched in his open cockpit, lifted his goggles and wiped his eyes, tired from the strain. When he looked out again, the horizon ahead sprouted a jagged line of land. He smoothed the navigation chart wth his mittened hand. Only a few isolated peaks were marked on Ellesmere Island. But what he saw on the horizon was definitely a tall mountain range.

As the two planes came closer, the mountains grew taller. Some of the peaks were covered with snow and seemed to melt with the bluish haze. Others, like enormous skyscrapers of bare rock, reached defiantly into the pale arctic sky, thousands of feet above the aircraft level. In the shallow saddles between the peaks squatted glaciers that blinded the flyers as with searchlights of the reflected sun rays.

Directing his pilot, Byrd vainly searched the hostile land below for a level landing place. Should the straining engine fail, the plane would crash against the iced rocks below. The water in the narrow fiords of the island was either packed with rough ice or strewn with drifting floe.

Then the wind below shifted, pulling the white curtain of clouds over the island. Byrd checked the fuel reserve. "Turn back for Etah," he wrote on a pad, and passed the message to the pilot.

The trip back was a race against the wind that now piled the low clouds ahead of the aircraft. Byrd spotted an opening below and patted the pilot's shoulder. The two planes dived through the opening just before it closed. Dodging the high cliffs, they leveled off over Smith Sound and skimmed the ice floe all the way to their Etah landing.

Byrd climbed out of the cockpit. In spite of their Eskimo boots lined with sheepskin, their polar-bear trousers and reindeer-skin jackets, the flyers shivered from cold.

MacMillan stamped his feet on the snow and slapped his stiff hands against his thighs. "This was magnificent," he said to Byrd. "Why, only a year ago on my last expedition here, we wallowed in snow thigh-deep, yelling at our dogs until our throats were raw and our voices gone. We sweated and half-froze to death to cover a few miles a day. Today we've discovered a mountain range and just got a little cold!"

Byrd nodded. He knew that only the aircraft could open the arctic wilderness to exploration.

MacMillan gently rubbed his cheeks. "Of course landing in these parts is something else again," he said. "You'd better hurry up with those advanced bases before the summer is over—you haven't much time left, you know."

Byrd and his men finally succeeded in landing on Ellesmere Island, although the strong prevailing winds and the shifting ice made the spot too dangerous and unreliable as a base.

On August 20 two small caches of food and gasoline were established and Byrd suggested a long flight to the edge of the Arctic Sea. However, MacMillan objected. "Etah Fiord froze last night," he said. "If you had to make a forced landing, your plane would be ice-locked for the long arctic winter. Your plans for a long flight north are out of the question."

That night MacMillan radioed the Navy Department that the conditions were too hazardous and that Byrd's air exploration should be stopped. "Landing places are few and food caches cannot be relied upon," he said in his message. "The lighter-than-air machines—dirigibles —can do the job and should do it at once."

Secretary of the Navy Wilbur radioed back, ordering Byrd to cancel his attempts to reach beyond Ellesmere Island. "Withdraw with MacMillan and make such secondary exploration by air as you deem practicable while the expedition returns south."

Byrd's aviation unit rebelled openly against this turn of events. "I'm sure we could still make it to Crocker Land—even to the Pole," Bennett argued hotly. "Why, we've proved that the planes and the engines can take it. Right?"

"Right!" echoed Schur. "We've flown about six thousand miles—we've covered some thirty thousand square miles of the territory. What does old Mac know about flying!"

"Yeah, just give the word, Commander," another cut in. "We'll fly with you—MacMillan willin' or not!"

Byrd raised his hand, commanding silence. "I can never tell you what your loyalty means to me," he said evenly. "But, gentlemen, we are in the United States Navy. I won't have a dissent on this expedition. I want you to obey Commander MacMillan's orders implicitly and without criticism. Any complaints will be submitted in writing and through channels after we land back in New York."

In New York, Byrd learned about Amundsen's new-planned expedition to the North Pole. "Come on, Bennett," he said. "Unless you've changed your mind about flying to the Pole with me, let's go to Washington and start the ball rolling."

Within a few days Secretary Wilbur granted Byrd and Bennett a six months leave of absence. Byrd's friends in the Shipping Board lent him the three-thousand-ton steamer *Chantier*. Edsel Ford and John D. Rockefeller, Jr., again contributed money toward the purchase of a new tri-motor Fokker plane, food, and supplies. And Byrd settled down to planning his arctic expedition.

Going over the budget with Byrd, Bennett said, "You mean we are going to spend one hundred and forty thousand dollars for that one flight?"

"Well, we haven't quite got that much, Floyd. But if Ford and Rockefeller were willing to gamble twenty thousand apiece on our expedition, I am certainly willing to bet the rest if necessary. Don't you think the flight is worth it?"

"You can bet your life I do, Commander," Bennett said. "And I'd be willing to bet mine—I'd give it to you for the chance of going along."

9

IT WAS 3:00 P.M. ON APRIL 29, 1926. THE ENGINE ROOM telegraph bell rang and the *Chantier* shivered as the reversed propellers brought it to a gentle halt. Anchor chain rattled out and the ship silently swung into the wind, about a mile from the icy shore of Kings Bay, Spitsbergen.

Huddled in his parka, Commander Byrd leaned on the bridge rail. His blue-gray eyes squinted against the midnight sun as he looked toward the landing dock. Tied there was a small Norwegian gunboat, *Heimdahl*. "Captain Brennan, order a boat lowered," Byrd said. "I am going ashore to ask if they can move their ship and let us use the dock for a few hours. Meanwhile get the crew to prepare the aircraft for unloading."

Warming himself by a coal stove in the harbor shack, the skipper of the *Heimdahl* politely listened to Byrd's request. "I understand your problem, Commander," he said, "but moving my ship is out of the question. She is laid up for repairs."

"We'll tow her out into the channel," Byrd suggested. "And bring her right back, as soon as we have unloaded our aircraft."

The Norwegian shook his head. "Sorry, sir. We couldn't do it. A sudden shift of wind . . . and the ice pack would crush the ship's hull like an eggshell. Look at the bay," he said, pointing through the window. "Within half an hour that ice at the mouth of the harbor can pile into the channel solid. And nothing would stop it. I know these waters and I can't jeopardize the safety of my ship."

For a moment Byrd's face clouded. He had raced ten thousand storm-ridden miles from New York only to reach this stalemate. He had heard that Amundsen and his polar expedition were already at Kings Bay, waiting for their dirigible *Norge* and the flight to the North Pole. Surely there was a way to unload the *Josephine Ford* plane. There had to be. . . .

Suddenly a half-smile softened Byrd's intent expression. "Let's go back to our ship," he told his men. "And row like mad!"

Climbing up the ship's ladder, Byrd called for a "council of war" in his cabin. Excitedly he explained the predicament and his new plan. It was risky, perhaps dangerous, but it could be done.

"The *Chantier's* four lifeboats will be lowered and lashed together. On top, the carpenters will make a platform strong enough to support the tri-motored plane. The whole rig will then be rowed to shore."

Captain Brennan eyed Commander Byrd sternly.

"You're taking a terrible chance," he said. "A gust of wind, an ice floe—and there goes your plane and the expedition, not to mention our lifeboats."

Byrd smiled. "It can be done, Captain," he said quietly.

Floyd Bennett nodded his silent approval. Plainly it was the only thing to do.

For hours the *Chantier's* crew, under the direction of "Chips" Gould, the ship's carpenter, worked feverishly on the huge raft. Finally the boats were lowered and lashed together and the platform secured to their gunwales. The *Josephine Ford* was hoisted on deck and the crane was about to swing it over the ship's side when a snow squall hit.

A gusty gale slammed against the *Chantier's* hull and howled through the rigging. It caught the aircraft's wing, snapped the anchoring lines, and tilted the plane—threatening to smash it into the ship's superstructure.

Byrd was first to grab one of the broken ropes. Electrified by his example, the crew rushed to his aid and pulled on the ropes with all their might. For a few moments the life of the plane and the success of Byrd's expedition hung in a precarious balance as men and the gale struggled in the grim tug-of-war. Inch by inch, red-faced from the superhuman effort, the men pulled the seventy-four-foot wing down. The plane was safe.

While the aircraft was being tied down again with extra rope, someone yelled, "The raft!"

Buffeted by the wind and the choppy waves, the raft chafed at its mooring lines—coming within inches of crashing into the ship's hull. The crew rushed to the rescue. Bracing themselves against the gale, they brought the fragile raft astern where the *Chantier* served as a breakwater. Holding the raft off with boat hooks and continually checking the mooring lines, the men fought the storm for twelve hours.

Watching the struggle from shore, the Norwegian sailors sadly nodded their heads. "Maybe this will teach them a lesson or two about the Arctic. That man Byrd must be a fool."

Commander Byrd worked alongside his men, tightening the ropes, staving off the ice floes, and encouraging the crew to further effort. "The storm can't last forever. And if it doesn't abate soon, we'll take off right from the deck," he laughed.

As suddenly as it hit, the storm blew out to sea. The arctic sun peeked through the broken clouds on Commander Byrd and his crew, staggering after the long battle. The harbor was a shambles. Broken by the waves, the once-solid sheet of ice near the shore now cluttered the channel with razor-sharp ice floes.

"I guess we need an ice breaker," panted Floyd Bennett.

Commander Byrd nodded. "We certainly do." He looked at the exhausted crew. "Men, we must take the aircraft ashore at once. We can't rest now. There may be another storm brewing. Are you with me?"

Such was the magic Byrd held over those around him that the amateur sailors, dog-tired as they were, responded with a unanimous "Aye, aye, sir!"

"All right, then. Let's lower another boat and break the ice!"

Huffing and puffing clouds of vapor, the men in the "icebreaker" lifeboat hacked at the ice-floe cakes, shoved them out of the way, and cleared a broad path of water toward shore. In their wake the cumbersome raft with *Josephine Ford* perched on the platform inched its way forward as the oarsmen pulled in mighty rhythm.

Halfway to shore, Byrd, who was conning the raft from the bow, spotted a huge iceberg drifting into the bay on a collision course. A crash was inevitable.

"Boat ahoy!" Byrd yelled to his improvised-icebreaker crew. "We must stop that berg!"

The crew stopped rowing and gaped at the towering mountain of arctic ice bulldozing its way through the floes.

Byrd cupped his mittened hands around his mouth. "Get back to the ship—get dynamite—blast the berg—hurry!"

The raft now reached the end of the laboriously cleared path and jarred against the ice. Mentally calculating the minutes before the berg would be upon them, Byrd calmly watched the impromptu demolition squad stumble and skid on the slippery iceberg. Floyd Bennett edged toward Byrd. "How about the blast?" he asked evenly. "The blown-up ice pieces might damage the plane."

The men had lodged the dynamite. Trailing the fuse wires, they scuttled for their boat and frantically rowed away. The berg now loomed ominously, so close to the raft and the plane that Byrd could feel its icy breath on his face. He glanced at his watch and, pursing his lips, appraised the shrinking distance. "If the Almighty doesn't want us to get to the North Pole, we'll know within a few seconds," he said.

Lowered into a deep crack in the iceberg, the dynamite

charge exploded with a basso rumble. Bennett held his breath. Byrd's lips moved in silent prayer.

The face of the berg cracked with a loud report, split apart in a wide *Y*. Then the two sides smashed together, sending a plume of ice crystals high into the sky. There was a gurgle of water. A wave ran through the floes, grinding and mashing the ice into a green-gray slush. The giant berg was gone.

Byrd shook off the ice dust settling on his wavy hair. "Well, I guess we'll make it," he said, smiling.

When the raft ground to a stop on the shore, the crew of the Norwegian gunboat burst into a rousing cheer. There was a commotion on deck; then some sailors brought out accordions, trumpets, and drums and spontaneously played the "Star Spangled Banner."

As Byrd's plane was rolled on top of a small snow-covered hill, the great Norwegian Arctic explorer Amundsen and his men came in force to greet their American rivals in the polar race.

Byrd and Amundsen shook hands. "Come to my headquarters," said the Norwegian, his bronzed face creased in a friendly smile. "We must drink a toast to your success."

"And to yours," Byrd answered.

Meanwhile Byrd's crew set up the camp, hacking a shelter in the ice and building a small lean-to. For five days Byrd, Noville, Bennett, and their chief mechanic, "Doc" Kinkade, worked practically around the clock— checking the plane, the engines and bringing the supplies from *Chantier*. Amundsen's dirigible *Norge* was expected any day and the race was close.

Finally, on May 3, "Doc" Kinkade switched off the

purring engines and said, "Commander, she's all set."

Byrd and Bennett climbed into the cockpit. Byrd nodded. "Let's take her on a test hop," he said. Bennett checked the instruments, started the engines, and shoved the throttles forward. The plane freed its skis frozen to the ice, then slid downhill on its take-off run. It bounced and joggled to the powerful song of the motors at full power. Suddenly the mighty roar broke off.

The echo was still reverberating among the icy hills as the aircraft dipped its wing and skidded sideways to a halt halfway down the runway. Byrd was first out of the cabin. He bent over the broken ski, probing and testing the fragile structure. "It's a miracle," he said with a sigh of relief. "Just the ski is broken; everything else— the rest of the landing gear—seems all right!"

Exhausted to the point of collapse, Byrd and his crew dug the plane out of the snow, hauled it up the hill, and started fitting a spare ski. Watching the repairs was a tall, husky Norwegian. He examined the plane's skis critically and said, "Excuse me, Commander. My name is Bernt Balchen. I am with the Amundsen–Ellsworth expedition."

Byrd looked up, returning the greeting.

"Perhaps I can help you prevent another broken ski," Balchen said. "We've had the same trouble in Norway. What you need is a mixture of paraffin and tar—smear it on your skis before the take-off."

Gratefully Byrd took the stranger's advice. Moreover, he led his men in building a longer runway and smoothing the bumps to lessen the shocks to the landing gear. And by the end of the day the plane was ready for another trial.

This time the take-off was smooth. The engines and the plane worked perfectly and Byrd decided to start loading the plane for his "dash" to the Pole.

The *Josephine Ford* gulped down enough fuel to last for 22 hours of flight. In the fuselage, men lashed down spare clothes and emergency food rations—enough for ten weeks, in case the plane should be forced down in the polar wilderness. Byrd, always a careful planner, had designed a special inflatable rubber raft which would save their lives in case he and Bennett had to ditch their plane in the Arctic Sea. Also lashed down securely in the fuselage was a light sledge for lugging the supplies—a "good luck" present from Amundsen.

The fueling and loading was finished none too soon, for the dirigible *Norge* poked its cigar shape into the valley and majestically landed in front of its special hangar a few hundred feet away from Byrd's plane.

A day later, word reached Byrd that the *Norge* was almost ready to go. Byrd looked toward the giant hangar. "Well, we're ready too. Let's go, Bennett."

The warmed-up engines responded readily. Bennett kicked the rudder pedals to keep the plane on the smoothed runway. Byrd clenched his hands on the sides of his cockpit seat. The plane started downhill. Catapulated by a bump, it left the ground, staggered clumsily and slammed down again, covering itself with a cloud of snow.

Biting his lips, Bennett pulled the control yoke back. Reluctantly the plane's nose lifted, but the wings still lacked the precious lift. The aircraft stalled, settled on the runway. Bennett shook his head. He chopped the throttles and the engine roar died. The plane skidded into a snowdrift. "Sorry, Commander—she's too heavy."

Silent, his fact set in grim determination, Byrd took over the controls and taxied the plane back up the hill. "We'll have to toss some of our supplies out," he said. "Come on, Bennett, bear a hand."

Out went some two hundred pounds of emergency rations and over one hundred pounds of souvenirs the expedition members had secreted in the plane for the trip to the Pole. Going over the fuel-consumption figures carefully calculated for the 1360-mile flight, Byrd said, "We'll have to leave some of our reserve fuel too." About five hundred gallons of gasoline in cans were handed down from the fuselage and dropped into the snow.

While part of the crew lightened the aircraft, other men iced up the runway, to further lessen the ski friction, and tied the tail skid of the plane to a stake. Now the pilot would be able to run the engines to full power, give a signal for the anchoring rope to be cut, and thus gain several precious feet of the take-off run.

In the navigator's seat Byrd, hunched over the weight chart, scribbled figures, crossing them out and writing again. His eyelids, swollen from lack of sleep in the past three days, weighted heavily. Finally his head dropped on his chest and he slept.

Three hours later, at 1:00 A.M. on May 9, "Doc" Kinkade shook Byrd awake. The weather was perfect. It was time to try again.

Once more the engines were warmed up and the plane carefully checked. At 1:58 A.M. Floyd Bennett revved up the engines to full power and gave the sign out the cockpit window. Poised with an ax, by the plane's tail, one of the men cut the anchoring rope. The *Josephine Ford* shot down the runway.

Bennett held the plane on the runway. The end of the cleared path rushed close. His eyes fixed on the pile of broken ice ahead, Byrd held his breath. The crash seemed inevitable. Then Bennett pulled the yoke back. The plane lifted . . . zoomed over the piled ice with only inches to spare.

They climbed to two thousand feet and set course—360 degrees North. The midnight sun sparkled on the sea and the ice floe, filling the cramped cockpit with dancing reflections.

An hour passed. The engines droned on; the fuselage picked up their mighty hum and shivered with anticipation. One hundred miles behind the plane the hills of Spitsbergen melted into the smoke-blue mist.

Byrd nudged Bennett and pointed below. They were crossing over the edge of the polar ice pack. The white expanse, marbled with pressure ridges in an intricate pattern, stretched ahead to the horizon and beyond.

Taking turns at piloting the plane, the two men caught an occasional cat nap. Byrd slept fitfully, awaking with a start after a few minutes of dozing. Apart from relieving Bennett at the controls, he had to navigate—check the wind drift and plot the course. So close to the magnetic pole of the earth, the magnetic compass, swirling to and fro, was of no use. But, prepared for this, Byrd had his sextant—a sun compass; and the sun was high in the sky, even at 4:00 A.M.

Looking out the cabin window of his navigation compartment, Byrd noticed a black rivulet of oil on the starboard engine. Oil leak! He wrote a message on the pad and passed it to his companion. Bennett checked the oil-pressure gauge, speculatively stared at the leak, and scribbled, "That engine is bound to quit!"

Byrd bent over the chart. They were within an hour's flight of the Pole. They had to get there—turning back was out of the question, for only at the Pole could they fix their position accurately enough by the sun compass to plot their return course for Spitsbergen. Byrd scribbled another message: "We have to go on."

Bennett wrote a reply: "Let's land and fix the darned leak before we do—before that engine quits."

Byrd read the slip and looked down. The pressure ridges were so close now that there was not enough smooth ice for a safe landing. He wrote hurriedly: "Too risky to land. If we have to crash, it may as well be on the North Pole."

Relieving Bennett at the controls, Byrd kept his eyes glued to the fluctuating oil-pressure gauge. It was bound to drop any moment. The needle started down, then crept up, playing a deadly cat-and-mouse game. Bennett couldn't rest. Scraping the frost off the cabin window, he fixed his eyes on the engine—now covered with black oil.

Back at his navigating table, Byrd checked his calculations and then wrote: "We made it! Our dream has come true at 9:02 A.M. Greenwich mean time!"

In the excitement of the moment the two pilots forgot the starboard engine. Bracing himself against the table, Byrd took a sight on the sun . . . then another. He scribbled figures on the margin of his chart. Yes, this was it. They were at the top of the world!

"Let's make a trip around the world," Byrd wrote. Bennett nodded and smiled broadly, banking the plane in a shallow turn. In four minutes the plane described a perfect circle around the North Pole. "May 9, 1926—around the world in 240 seconds," Byrd scribbled. The men looked at each other and burst out laughing, like two small boys enjoying a classroom prank.

At 9:15 A.M. Byrd reluctantly wrote: "Let's go back." Bennett banked the plane steeply to set course for Spitsbergen, but in his excitement, or perhaps fatigue, he let the plane slip in its path. Byrd's sextant slid off the table and crashed to the floor. The only means of navigating was now damaged beyond repair.

But Byrd was an expert navigator. Luckily he had fixed their position on the Pole and now decided to navigate by dead reckoning—finding the air speed from the indicator and the course by heading directly into the sun. "If my figuring is correct," he wrote, "we'll hit land at Grey Hook."

Bennett watched the quivering needle of the oil gauge. "What's the gas situation?"

"Barely enough," answered Byrd. "Let's pray for a tail wind."

With over half of the fuel gone, their plane was several hundred pounds lighter. If the starboard engine should fail, perhaps they could make it on the two remaining engines. On the other hand, the added drag of a dead engine would slow the plane down. If only the wind would shift to push them along . . .

Byrd fell asleep murmuring a prayer. When he awoke, he looked at the ailing engine and rubbed his bloodshot eyes in disbelief. The glistening black patches of the leaking oil were no longer ripped by the air stream. The oil patches were frozen. And since the engine still worked perfectly, the leak must have stopped. He nudged Bennett and yelled in his ear, "The engine! It's a miracle!"

At 4:20 A.M., peering through the windshield, Byrd noticed a gray, wavy smudge on the misty horizon. He shook Bennett awake. "Land ahead!"

Ten minutes later Bennett relieved Byrd at the controls and brought the *Josephine Ford* to a bumpy landing at Kings Bay. Amundsen and his men rushed across the snow to greet their successful rivals. Embracing Byrd, the old Norwegian explorer said, "In a few hours you have accomplished what has taken me my lifetime. . . . I am so happy for you."

Numb from fatigue and cold, Byrd could not make his mouth work. He nodded acknowledgment and, helped by his cheering mechanics, stumbled to the *Chantier* to sleep.

On May 20 the *Chantier* steamed out of Kings Bay. Relaxing in his cabin, Byrd listened to the news from the outside world. Chamberlin, Davis, Nungesser, and Fonck —each was planning a transatlantic flight.

Byrd looked at Bennett. "You know, Floyd, I think those men have something there," he said. "We've proved that flight over the Arctic is possible. Within thirty years I am sure there'll be airliners flying a North Pole route to Europe. But I think the Atlantic air routes will have to come first, don't you?"

"Sure do." Bennett smiled. "You wouldn't be thinking of making a hop from New York to Paris, would you?"

Byrd was deep in his thoughts. "Hmm . . . maybe we could prove that a big passenger plane could safely cross the Atlantic."

"I hope you can take me with you," Bennett said anxiously.

"We go together, Floyd."

10

ON JUNE 23, 1926, AS BYRD AND BENNETT STEPPED ashore in New York harbor, tugs tooted their stentorian greeting to the heroes, fireboats gushed tons of spray skyward, and several bands tried to outplay one another in an excited cacophony. Byrd hardly had time to hug his lovely wife, Marie, before he was hustled into an open car and driven along lower Broadway.

Crowds cheered, pushed, and jostled the cordons of sweating policemen. Ticker tape, and telephone directories torn to shreds, floated down in the hot and humid June air.

Bewildered and speechless, the two pilots listened to the orations at City Hall, received scrolls, shook thousands of eager hands. And that afternoon, under heavy police escort, they made their way to Pennsylvania Station and the train for Washington, D.C.

Thousands of distinguished citizens, foreign diplomats, scientists, and reporters crowded the Washington auditorium. There were more speeches and tumultuous ovations. Under Klieg lights and photographers' flash bulbs, President Coolidge presented the two men with the top award of the National Geographic Society—the Hubbard Gold Medal.

Then Byrd was called upon to speak. Staggered by the reception, he nevertheless was in full control of himself. In well-measured words he sketched out his expedition simply, as though reporting on a routine naval mission. Typically he pointed up only the effort of his colleagues. "They made me proud to be one of them. . . . I receive this medal thinking of them and my flying mate here, Floyd Bennett, who deserves credit above any one of us. As for me—what I have been capable of I owe to the Navy. All my training came from her."

The auditorium exploded in standing applause. He bowed his head and stiffly walked to his chair of honor, next to the blushing and perspiring Bennett.

"If I had known we'd have to go through all this," murmured Bennett out of the corner of his mouth, "I'd have thought twice before going to the Pole with you. Couldn't we sneak out of here somehow?"

Later, in his hotel room, Byrd threw himself on his bed. His windburned neck was sore from the stiff collar of his dress uniform, and his head was still buzzing. "I'd give anything to go home," he said to his wife. "How is Dickie? And the girls? And baby Helen?"

Marie gently stroked his hair. "They are just fine," she said lovingly. "We've all missed you, of course, but I and

103

the children understand—we are so terribly proud of you, more than words can express."

Byrd closed his eyes and his tension relaxed under his wife's caress. He sighed. "I'm afraid we'll have to separate again soon, darling. First I'll have to go on a lecture tour —make some money. Goodness knows, we need it. Then—"

"You'll fly the Atlantic?"

Byrd sat up. "How did you know?"

Marie smiled. "Woman's intuition, I suppose. I've known it ever since that flight to Europe, years ago—the one you didn't quite make." She turned so that her husband could not see the shadow of concern on her face. "Are you going to race Lindbergh and the others?"

"Oh no, Marie—certainly not." Byrd shed fatigue and perked up, as always when talking about his pioneering dreams. "It's going to be a passenger flight, not a record-breaking stunt. We'll fly a multi-engined plane—a prototype of future airliners."

He told her about scheduled flights that someday would link the world's cities, about dependable and swift air-mail, cargo and medicines rushed to any part of the globe in a matter of hours, cultural exchange that would promote world peace. He lay back, with his muscular arms crossed under his head. As he went far into the future, his voice slowly trailed into silence—as though he were overwhelmed by his daring vision.

"Whatever you want to do, darling, I am with you all the way," Marie said.

Byrd was breathing rhythmically. He didn't hear her; nor did he see her eyes, glistening with tears.

In the midst of his grueling, town-a-day lecture tour,

a telegram summoned him and Bennett to the Capitol again to receive more awards. The American Geographical Society created a special honor for Byrd—they made him Doctor of Longitude and Latitude. Congress promoted him to full Commander and Bennett to Aviation Machinist. And on February 25, 1927, President Coolidge presented the polar aviators with the Congressional Medal of Honor for "conspicuous courage and intrepidity at the risk of their lives." The citation ranked their flight "with the accomplishments of Marco Polo, Columbus, and Amundsen's discovery of the South Pole."

After the ceremony Byrd hustled Bennett to a quiet corner. "Rodman Wanamaker has already given us his financial backing," he said, completely forgetting the nation's highest award they had received only minutes before. "Also I talked to Fokker. He is working on a new plane for us—three-engined and bigger than the old *Josephine*. It will carry enough fuel for forty hours of flight with half a ton of payload and a crew of four."

"Terrific!" Bennett's eyes shone with excitement. "Say, who are the other two men?"

"Lieutenant Noville, of course, and a Norwegian fellow as your copilot—Bernt Balchen. Remember him?"

"How can I forget?" Bennett chuckled. "Without that guy's advice we'd still be sitting frozen to that runway at Kings Bay!"

Before they parted, Byrd said, "We'll probably be taking off sometime in May. I'll pull you to New York as soon as I wind up my tour and get some rest at home, Floyd."

The few days' rest Byrd allowed himself at his Boston home passed all too quickly. He hugged his children, kissed Marie good-bye, and with his battered briefcase bulging with papers he rushed to the train. Unrecognized by his fellow passengers, he studied the fuel-consumption charts of his new engines. He was so engrossed in his work that he didn't realize the train had arrived at its destination and that all the passengers had left.

The conductor tapped Byrd gently on the shoulder. "Grand Central Station, sir." Then he did a double-take. "Say, haven't I seen you somewhere before?"

Byrd flashed a smile. "Could be," he said. "I travel a great deal."

The nominal headquarters of Byrd's planned expedition were in a small room at the Hotel McAlpin in Manhattan. However, Byrd was seldom there. He spent most of his time several miles across the Hudson—in a small, busy factory in Hasbrouck Heights, New Jersey, the birthplace of his new aircraft, the *America.*

On April 14 Bennett rushed into the hangar waving a newspaper. "Look at this!" he said. "Bert Acosta and Clarence Chamberlin have just set a new record—fifty-one hours and eleven minutes' flight, nonstop!"

Byrd, Noville, and Fokker gathered around, reading the front-page news over each other's shoulders. "Well, that's about four hours more than it'll take us to get to Paris," Byrd said. "It means that our engines can take it, all right."

The group walked to the aircraft that crowded the hangar with its varnished plywood wings. Byrd patted the fuselage fabricspanned like a tom-tom. "As far as I know, none of the transatlantic planes are ready yet," he said, his blue-gray eyes twinkling with a mischievous smile. "What do you say we take our baby for a test hop tomorrow? We're not in the 'Transatlantic Derby,' but beating the others to Paris would not be a bad thing."

The next day, mechanics rolled the *America* out of the hangar. As proud as a father of his first-born, Fokker himself checked every control cable and every fastener on the engines' cowling. He climbed into the cockpit with Byrd, Bennett, and Noville following.

One by one the engines came to life. Feeling the control yoke and the rudder pedals, Fokker waved the chocks away. As he pushed the throttles forward, the balloon tires thumped along the turf runway . . . faster, faster, until the plane's snub nose gracefully pointed upward.

Fokker beamed. "Smooth, eh?"

He put his machine through its paces, climbing, turning, and wheeling around. Then he eased the throttles back, heading for the runway. Suddenly the plane pitched nose-down, as though a powerful hand lifted its tail.

"*Himmel!*" Fokker shoved the throttles forward, pulling back on the yoke. The plane recovered a few feet off the ground, the straining engines dragging it up again to safety.

At higher altitude this time, Fokker shut off the power. Again the plane plunged out of control. Sweat glistened on Fokker's bald pate as he recovered. Byrd glanced at the fuel gauges. "We haven't much time," he shouted. "What do you think is wrong?"

Fokker shrugged. "Wrong balance!"

Byrd looked back. If only they could get to the rear fuselage . . . The few hundred pounds of weight, if shifted to the tail, might help keep the plane on an even keel. But the huge fuselage tank barred the way. They had to crash.

107

Skillfully Fokker glided toward the landing field at half-power. One hundred feet off the ground, he yelled, "Watch out!" He closed the throttles.

The plane nosed down. The tires squealed under the impact. The nose propeller bit into the grass. The aircraft slammed the ground with a thud. The impact hurled Bennett, Byrd, and Noville forward, while Fokker catapulted out of the plane through the overhead hatch. The aircraft bounced. Fabric tore with a dry screech as the machine parabolaed and crashed on its back in a cloud of dust.

Wedged under the hot engine, Bennett called, "Get out —she'll catch fire!"

Noville ripped the fuselage fabric, crawled out, and collapsed. Byrd, his right arm strangely numb, followed him through the gaping hole. "Floyd!" he shouted, looking back at the wreckage.

A moan of pain came from the crumpled cabin. Bennett was trapped inside.

Oblivious of the arm hanging uselessly at his side Byrd scrambled back into the wreck. His powerful left arm bent the tubing, shoved the jumbled equipment aside as he fought his way in. Mechanics followed Byrd with metal shears and crowbars. They extricated the unconscious Bennett and gingerly carried him to a car. Miraculously the plane did not catch fire.

On the way to the hospital, holding Floyd's battered head in his lap, Byrd realized that his right arm was broken. Biting his lips until they bled, he set his arm in the joggling car. In spite of the crash and the injury of his dear friends, the aircraft had to be rebuilt and the flight plan carried out. "I can't afford the delay," he told Fokker, who had escaped without a scratch.

Ten days after the *America's* crash, the "Transatlantic Derby" opened officially when Commander Davis took off in his *American Legion* from Langley Field, Virginia. Overloaded, the plane fell out of the sky after taking off and crashed, killing the brave crew.

Repairs to the *America* were in full swing. Byrd commuted between Bennett's bedside and the Fokker workshop, while newspapers speculated on his chances in the race. Then Nungesser and Coli lifted their *White Bird* off the ground at Le Bourget, Paris, and headed for the United States. Somewhere over the Atlantic they vanished without a trace, and suddenly the eager public turned against the long overwater flights.

Byrd's McAlpin Hotel headquarters were swamped with mail and telegrams urging him to abandon the suicidal flight. But Byrd was adamant about his plans. "Of course there's some danger in a transatlantic flight," he told his well-wishers. "But only by trying again can we find out what happened to the missing French aviators and plan to avoid the mistakes they may have made. I have a job to do and I am going to see it through."

By mid-May the *America* was ready again. Fokker had corrected the plane's trim and it passed its initial test flights. But this time Byrd decided to test the plane until all conceivable chances of failure were eliminated. He landed *America* at Roosevelt Field, Long Island, and let his old arctic crew, "Doc" Kinkade and Tom Mulroy, groom the plane.

George O. Noville got out of the hospital and Byrd's broken arm healed. But Bennett was definitely out of the game. Looking for another first pilot, Byrd learned that Bert Acosta had just quit Bellanca's camp. He hired him on the spot.

The *America* was being officially christened at Roosevelt Field when news flashed that Lindbergh had landed safely at Le Bourget. Again public criticism turned on Byrd. A stranger wired him: "You're the world's prize boob to get left asleep at the switch." Another man wrote: "You're a coward. What are you waiting for?"

Even Harry Byrd, the new governor of Virginia, who came to see his brother Dick off, could not understand why he insisted on flying the Atlantic right after Lindbergh. "I wish you could explain that to me, Dick," he said.

Byrd passed his fingers through his wavy, graying hair. "Well, Harry, Lindbergh proved that an airplane can span the Atlantic, all right. But I am going to demonstrate that a transatlantic flight is more than a stunt." He started to pace his hotel room. "We are going to carry eight hundred pounds of mail. Do you see what that means? Payload, Harry, payload—almost half a ton— imagine! That's what we are going to prove—the feasibility of commercial airplane flight between the United States and Europe."

Byrd kept testing his plane daily and methodically prepared for take-off. Remembering how the downhill take-off at Kings Bay had helped get the *Josephine Ford* off the ground, he had earth piled into a ramp on the edge of the airfield. In case one of the outboard engines should develop an oil leak or some other trouble, Byrd's mechanics fastened special catwalks to the plane so that each engine could be reached and possibly repaired in flight. And while "Doc" Kinkade pampered the engines, Byrd daily checked the weather situation with the U. S. Weather Bureau in Washington.

Tired, Byrd went to bed at 2:00 A.M. on June 28. One hour later a telephone call from the Weather Bureau sent him to the hangar. The weather was about as good as it could be, said the report.

Plodding through the drizzle, Byrd and his flight crew reached their plane, already posed at the top of the ramp its tail tied to a stake. Acosta slid into the pilot's seat. Noville sat behind him, his hand on the fuel-dump valve that could drain all twelve hundred gallons of gas in a matter of seconds and lighten the plane should there be trouble on take-off. Bernt Balchen's station was in the fuselage, in front of the fuel tank. Byrd sat next to Acosta in the cockpit.

Acosta revved up the engines. The fifteen-thousand-pound aircraft shivered and strained against the rope as Tom Mulroy, knife in hand, waited for the pilot's signal to cut. And the signal never came. Weakened by moisture, the rope snapped and the plane rolled down the runway, splashing through the puddles like a scared duck on the run.

The engines had not been sufficiently warmed up and the plane was sluggish. Acosta raised his hand—a stand-by signal for Noville to dump the fuel. Byrd held his breath. Acosta pulled back on the yoke with his left hand. It responded. He lifted his thumb—they were off!

Balchen let out a triumphant yell that drowned the engines' roar. But Byrd's and Acosta's eyes were on the altimeter. Would the plane climb with all that load? Momentarily Byrd regretted the eight hundred pounds of mail he had taken on board. Then he reflected that by leaving the mail behind he would have defeated the purpose of the flight.

The altimeter needle seemed glued to zero. Slowly it flicked up a notch. The plane was climbing.

The drizzle turned to rain when the plane reached three thousand feet on course. In the fuselage Bernt Balchen worked like a stoker of a steamship. As the engines gulped the fuel from the main tank, he emptied extra fuel into it from five-gallon cans and threw the empties overboard.

While Byrd navigated, measured the wind drift, and checked the course, George Noville worked the radio set and kept an eye on the fuel consumption. The plane had just reached Nova Scotia—the last land before their jump-off on the two thousand-mile overwater stretch to France—when Byrd asked for a fuel check.

Noville scribbled the figures and passed the pad. Byrd checked and rechecked the calculations, then wrote: "The slightest head wind and we'll run out of fuel before we reach the French coast. How is the weather back home?"

"Fog. We can't turn back," answered Noville.

Byrd leaned back and closed his eyes. If his study of upper winds was correct, they could just make it. But what if the theory of the prevailing westerly winds over the ocean was wrong? Should he tell the rest of the crew about the chances he was taking? Balchen would probably agree to go ahead, but temperamental Acosta might only get upset.

"Let's keep the fuel situation quiet," Byrd scribbled on the pad.

Noville nodded, crumpled the notes and stuffed them into his pocket.

The day faded into night. Blue flame of the engines' exhaust cast a ghostly pallor on the tired faces of the four men. Climbing to higher altitude, where Byrd hoped to find the lifesaving tail wind, the plane was swallowed by dense clouds. Occasionally air turbulence shook the machine; startled the pilot from his somnolence, making his eyes blink in surprise.

A painful cramp gnawed at Byrd's leg. He left the seat to stretch; but when he leaned against the fuselage tank, his fingers felt a familiar slick moisture. Gasoline leak? As though nothing had happened, he shone his flashlight. At the bottom of the tank a narrow stream of the precious fuel shimmered in the beam.

Calmly Byrd reached for the special putty he had taken for just such an emergency. Balchen was flying. Acosta tore into a fried chicken and Noville dozed at his radio table. Byrd squeezed the putty into the leaky seam. The gasoline stream tapered off into a dribble . . . the internal pressure must have been too much for the flimsy plug.

Morning light sneaked into the noise-drenched cockpit. Casually Byrd checked the fuel leak. It had stopped. This could mean only one thing, he reasoned. Noville's calculations were right and now the tank was almost empty.

Static crackling in the headset awoke Noville, and Byrd asked him to recheck the fuel consumption. He had to know the worst.

Noville scribbled for a few minutes and then, red-faced, handed Byrd the pad. "I made a mistake the first figuring. We have enough gas to take us to Rome. Sorry."

Sorry! Byrd burst out laughing. Startled, Acosta scratched his heavy dark stubble and smiled vacantly.

"Let's celebrate!" Byrd shouted.

Acosta nodded, always willing to go along with a gag. He motioned to Noville to pass him another fried chicken.

The engines roared happily. Noville contacted a couple of steamers below and got a fix. The *America* had had a thirty-mile-an-hour tail wind all the way from Newfoundland! Byrd's theory of playing the winds for added distance and speed was correct.

By afternoon of the second day the exhausted crew cheered at sight of the French coast. They hit it exactly as Byrd had planned. But their cheers faded when Noville got Paris weather on the radio—dense fog at Le Bourget.

After the glimpse of land, the plane barged into rain and clouds which thickened with the approaching darkness. Acosta tapped the sticky needle of his earth-inductor compass. It flickered but stood still. He flew on.

Byrd wrote: "Watch out for the beacon and lights. We should be approaching Paris." He had no sooner passed the message to Acosta than a revolving light blinked a friendly greeting through the cloud below.

While Byrd prepared a message to be radioed to New York announcing their arrival, Acosta circled the beacon. Suddenly the clouds broke. As the beam wiped the darkness, wavelike ripples reflected the powerful light with a twinkling shower of stars. This was a coastal lighthouse!

Checking the measured wink of the lighthouse against his charts, Byrd pinpointed the place—Ver-Sur-Mer. Evidently, steering by the stuck needle of his compass, Acosta had described a perfect circle.

Quickly Byrd calculated the course for Paris by the

stand-by compass. Acosta leveled the plane and headed into the heavy rain and darkness. Every few minutes Byrd checked the compass, the course, and the time. The farther they pushed inland, the worse the storm. Rain beat so hard against the windshield that Acosta couldn't have seen a beacon if there had been one.

"Paris in five minutes!" Byrd shouted into Acosta's ear.

Acosta cursed. He opened the side window and thrust his head into the rain-drenched, howling darkness. Water streaming down his neck, his hair knotted, he tried again and again, hoping to catch a glimpse of light from the ground.

"Paris below!"

Noville's radio beep-beeped: "Fog and rain at Le Bourget."

Obeying Acosta's firm pressure, the plane banked in a circle. The pilot now defied the elements. Lashed with rain, Acosta held his head out of the window as the powerful slip stream rammed his curses down his throat.

It was hopeless. But the storm-tossed plane had to land somewhere. Byrd grasped Acosta by the shoulder. "Turn back!" he shouted. "Ver-Sur-Mer!"

Defeated by the darkness and the two sleepless nights, Acosta slumped in his seat. "Take over, Bernt."

"Fuel?"

Noville hit the tank with his fist. It echoed ominously —almost empty.

Bent over his charts, Byrd figured the course . . . guessed at the wind drift. His hand jerked by the gusts, he wrote in the logbook: "One chance in a million for a safe landing."

Two and a half hours later, Bernt Balchen spotted the

lighthouse glare. Feeling his way through the clouds, he glided the plane and at one hundred feet they burst out of the dark mist.

Moving the unconscious Acosta out of the way, Byrd sat next to Balchen. Throttled-down engines backfired in an erratic staccato.

"Drop the flares, George!"

Noville responded like high-precision machinery. The flares hit the back surf and burned in a pool of blinding light.

"Stand by to land!"

The plane nosed into the brightness like a giant moth. Balchen cut the power. The dead engines left a vacuum of silence. The landing gear ripped off. A wave sizzled on the hot engine. CRASH!

On June 29, 1927, after forty-two hours of flight, the *America* dived into the sea, which punched through the the flimsy fabric with a hungry gurgle.

11

THE IMPACT OF THE CRASH HURLED BYRD AGAINST A bulkhead and momentarily knocked the breath out of him. Dazed and aching, he extricated himself from the rapidly sinking aircraft. "George! Bernt! Acosta!" he called, swimming along the fuselage.

The lighthouse beam swept the black sea. A few feet ahead of Byrd, George Noville surfaced, spitting like an angry walrus. He climbed on top of the wing and feverishly tore at the emergency-compartment hatch. Balchen and Acosta were nowhere in sight.

Ignoring the choking pain in his chest, Byrd dived. Balchen had already smashed the window open and was now kicking his way out. Both he and Byrd popped to the surface together.

Byrd shook Balchen by the shoulders. "Acosta . . . still inside!"

They dived again. Feeling their way around the dark, flooded cockpit, they found it empty. Again they surfaced and grabbed the slippery edge of the wing, panting.

Noville had the emergency compartment open. He pulled out the rubber dinghy and began inflating it.

The wing was now flush with the waves. Byrd and Balchen hoisted themselves on top, vainly peering into the darkness for some sign of the missing Acosta.

"Hey, there!" a strangely high-pitched voice called from the wingtip. "Is this the Staten Island ferry?"

Byrd crawled toward the voice, grasped Acosta's hand and helped him out of the water. The next sweep of the lighthouse beam shone on the four partners in adventure —haggard, but happy to be alive and together.

They loaded the dinghy with their meager belongings and the U. S. mail. Balchen took the oars, and the crew of the *America* headed for shore.

"We should have gone straight to Rome," Acosta said. "We did have enough gas, didn't we?"

Byrd nodded. "We could have made it, of course. But I had told Wanamaker we were going to go to Paris." He spoke quietly, but the tone of his statement put up a firm barrier against any further discussion. "Besides, we have accomplished our mission. We did reach our destination and we will deliver the mail," he said. "We have proved that commercial transatlantic flights are feasible. In a few years, with an international weather-forecasting service, passengers and cargo will be shuttled between Europe and the States on schedule, as safely as on a train."

After a brief rest at the Ver-Sur-Mer lighthouse, the four airmen were on a train to Paris. Alerted by the light-

118

house keeper's telegram, the entire city turned out to welcome the American aviators.

The crowds at the Gare du Nord swarmed about the motorcade, pressing against the open car in which the four heroes sat. *"Vive Byrd! Vive Acosta ... Balchen ... Noville! Vive l'Amerique!"* they shouted, pushing the car along the streets.

Down the Champs Elysées and Rue de la Paix crawled the motorcade. Store windows and entire buildings were draped in American and French flags as Paris, the City of Cities, paid tribute to the courage and determination of Byrd and his crew.

The whirlwind welcome lasted a whole week. There was a reception at the Fédération Aeronautique Internationale; a meeting with Louis Blériot, the famous French aviator, first to fly across the English Channel; a visit to Napoleon's tomb at the Invalides; a presentation to Marshal Foch, the hero commander-in-chief of the French armed forces.

Then another motorcade triumphantly rode across France to Cherbourg harbor—where, after another string of parties and speeches, the four airmen boarded the *SS Leviathan* bound for New York.

While the celebrations continued on board, Byrd already was planning his next move. In his stateroom he and Bernt Balchen spent hours discussing a new enterprise—an expedition to Antarctica and a flight to the South Pole.

"We'll get another tri-motor plane," Byrd said. "Ships, sledges, dogs . . ."

Bernt Balchen grinned. "Sounds great, Dick. But how

119

about money? An expedition like that will cost an awful lot."

"It will," Byrd said seriously. "I estimate the cost at about one million dollars."

Balchen slapped his forehead. "What? And how do you propose to raise that kind of money?"

"I don't know yet." Byrd narrowed his blue-gray eyes. "But where there's a will, there's a way. I'll work on this as soon as we land in New York."

However, a ticker-tape welcome in New York City delayed his plans. And more delays came in rapid succession. President Calvin Coolidge summoned Byrd and his companions to Washington for an audience; then back in New York, at the Commodore Hotel, Secretary of the Navy Curtis D. Wilbur pinned the Distinguished Flying Cross on Commander Byrd's uniform.

Wined, dined, and cheered, Byrd did not forget his friend Floyd Bennett. Late one evening, after a strenuous dinner reception, he hailed a cab and rode to Bennett's Brooklyn home.

Still convalescing after his accident, Bennett eagerly received the news about the planned expedition to the South Pole. "I'll be on my feet soon," he said excitedly. Bennett took a deep breath, which brought on a coughing spell. His hand trembled as he held a handkerchief to his mouth.

Pretending not to notice this, Byrd said, "Take things easy for the rest of the summer anyway, Floyd. I have a book to write and I shall have to go on a lecture tour—I need the money to keep my family going. Meanwhile I want you in topflight condition for the antarctic battle." Byrd covered his concern for Bennett's health with a smile. "I hate to get tough with you," he said, "but get plenty of rest and don't rush things. That's an order."

The New Year of 1928 was only a few weeks old when Commander Byrd set up his Antarctic expedition headquarters in a small room on the fifteenth floor of the Putnam Building in New York City. The walls were covered with maps and charts, and the only desk was swamped with papers. Byrd, Balchen, Bennett, and Captain Hilton Railey, the expedition's business manager, huddled there long into the night, like staff officers planning a major battle.

Late one night, after the daily planning conference broke up, Byrd took Floyd Bennett on a long walk, something he did often. "It will do you good to exercise," he said. "Besides, a walk helps all the details fall into place."

Fifth Avenue was deserted except for an occasional policeman on his lonely beat. Striding along the wide sidewalks Byrd spoke: "You know, after our North Pole flight, a friend of mine offered me an executive job in his company. Of course I turned it down. I didn't want to get involved in big business." He chuckled. "And look what we're doing now—we are organizing our expedition just like a big-business enterprise."

"Sure," Bennett said. "A million-dollar business—four ships, three aircraft, one snowmobile, and ninety-five dogs."

"And five hundred tons of supplies, from thumbtacks to pemmican," Byrd added.

They stopped on a corner, waited for a taxi to crawl by, then resumed their walk.

"There's one thing you didn't mention, Floyd," Byrd

continued. "It's the eighty-two men—the scientists, pilots, mechanics, and dog drivers. They are the most important ingredients of this or any other expedition. Our physical preparations are important, of course, but it's the men's loyalty to our common purpose that will make the difference between success and failure."

For a block the two men walked in silence, trailing the wispy vapor of their breath in the crisp winter air. Then Bennett spoke again. "How are we doing for funds, Dick?"

"Not too well. The reconditioning of our ships, the *City of New York* and the *Eleanor Bolling*, took more than we anticipated—three hundred thousand dollars."

"How much do we have in the kitty?"

Byrd calculated aloud. "Well, Charles Bob donated one hundred and eight thousand; Edsel Ford and John D. Rockefeller, Jr., contributed some three hundred thousand, and I have promises from others worth some one hundred thousand dollars."

"Isn't that enough?"

"Not by a long shot." Byrd took a deep breath. "We are in debt about two hundred thousand dollars. And how I'm going to raise that money between now and September, I don't know. But if we don't sail by the end of that month it will mean waiting a full year for another antarctic summer."

They stopped at a small all-night restaurant on Broadway and ordered coffee. Warming his hands against his cup, Bennett said, "You know, Dick, what you're doing is not managing a big-business organization—it's more like commanding an army. You have a fleet and an air force; you have an enemy—the antarctic weather and the five million square miles of that unknown continent—"

"Yes, and I also have the responsibility for every man who goes along." Byrd's shoulders slumped imperceptibly, as though weighed down by his awareness of that responsibility. "I shall have it with me for nearly two years, without a moment's relief."

"Come on, cheer up." Bennett smiled. "You've got friends; you're not alone!"

"Floyd, I thank God every day for my friends—men like you. Without you and the others I couldn't accomplish anything. But when it comes to making decisions—assuming the responsibility for the planning—I am alone."

The early spring of 1928 found the preparations in top gear. August was set as the time for departure of the *City of New York*, a three-masted bark with auxiliary steam engine. Her wooden hull was thirty-four inches thick to withstand ice pressure. She was an ice ship—every inch of her 170 feet, from stem to stern.

In September the *Eleanor Bolling* would follow the *City* south. *Bolling*, a steel-hulled, eight-hundred-ton cargo vessel, was rather underpowered with her two-hundred-horsepower steam engine, but the best Byrd could get at the time.

Each ship would carry supplies—fuel, food, medicines, extra clothes, and building material for the permanent base Byrd had planned to establish on the Bay of Whales. He had chosen that location because it was the closest point of the antarctic shore to the South Pole. Besides, it was the closest to the supply base at Dunedin, New Zealand.

The two ships would rendezvous with two Norwegian whalers, the *C. A. Larsen* and the *Sir James Clark Ross*, in New Zealand before the final two-thousand-mile leg of the trip to the Bay of Whales.

The *Larsen*, being the biggest and the fastest, would serve as the "flagship," with Byrd and his staff on board. It would also carry the expedition's aircraft.

The largest of the three aircraft was the tri-motor Ford donated by Edsel Ford. In addition, Byrd had ordered a single-engined Fokker–Universal to serve as a support plane, and a smaller single-engined Fairchild aircraft for scouting and liaison work.

Floyd Bennett and Bernt Balchen were given complete charge of the aircraft. They practically moved into the Ford plant in Detroit to supervise various modifications necessary to adapt the big plane to the extreme cold of Antarctica. By the first week of April, 1928, Bennett reported the plane ready.

"We trimmed the plane's weight by some five hundred pounds," Bennett said, happy as a schoolboy bringing home a good report card. "And, Dick, you'll have to fly her to believe it—she handles like a dream. And the three engines—imagine almost one thousand horsepower in front of you! We'll be shuttling between our base and the South Pole like the New York–Chicago mail planes— no trouble at all!"

"Wonderful!" Byrd slapped his friend on the back. "I knew I could depend on you, Floyd. I guess you've earned your unwritten title of 'second in command' of our expedition. Just hurry up with the final tests in Canada. And for goodness' sake, get rid of that cold of yours—stay in bed for a few days!"

"I will," Bennett said.

But a few days later the radio flashed the news about the crash of the *Bremen*—a German plane which had just crossed the Atlantic and was forced to land in Labrador.

Holding back his cough, Bennett telephoned Byrd's headquarters. "Dick, I think we could give our Ford plane a good shakedown cruise if we flew a rescue mission to the *Bremen*."

"Of course," Byrd said. "But how's your cold?"

"All better."

"Well, I only wish I could go with you; but I must do some more begging for funds here. Good luck and happy landings!"

Bennett and Balchen loaded fuel, spare parts, and supplies for their German fellow airmen and took off on the mercy flight. . . .

One day as he was leaving his headquarters for a money-raising conference, a Western Union messenger handed Byrd a telegram: BREMEN FLYERS RESCUED STOP BENNETT HOSPITALIZED WITH PNEUMONIA STOP CONDITION CRITICAL

Byrd ran to the phone. He canceled the conference and took the first train for Quebec. For forty-eight hours he sat at Bennett's bedside, but the great flyer's strength ebbed rapidly.

Propping himself on one shoulder, Bennett whispered hoarsely. "I guess I'll have to let you down, Dick—I'll be taking off for my last flight soon."

Byrd forced a smile. "Don't talk nonsense. Charles Lindbergh is flying serum from New York—the doctor says it will get the fever down at once."

125

"You're a poor liar, Dick." Bennett licked his parched lips. "All I need now are your prayers—and another big favor . . ." He reached under his pillow and handed Byrd his worn flying scarf. "Drop this at the South Pole for me . . . promise . . ."

Byrd's throat tightened. He quickly turned away, blinking hard. "I promise," he said. But Bennett did not hear, nor did he see the tears that rolled down Byrd's face.

Bennett's death was like a mortal wound to Byrd. His usual vitality, so necessary to conclude the final phase of planning the expedition, drained steadily. He lost his appetite, drew away from people, and either sat in his office staring out the window or went on long, lone walks.

"You've got to snap out of it, Dick," Captain Hilton Railey said. "Do you want to ruin this tremendous organization you've built? Do you want to fail so many of your friends and backers even before you start for the Pole?"

"Hilton, please, leave me alone."

"I won't. You can't let this expedition go to pot!"

Byrd buried his face in his hands and sat in silence. Then he let his arms drop as though they weighed a ton. "I'm sorry, Hilton," he said, "but the truth is, I don't care any more."

12

RAILEY SHRUGGED. "OKAY, DICK. AS YOU WISH." HE
started for the door, but turned before reaching it. "Did
it ever occur to you that, by mourning Bennett and neg-
lecting the planning work, you are actually letting Bennett down?"

Bennett's name brought the color of new life to Byrd's
face. Out of his breast pocket he brought a faded, neatly
folded flying scarf. Carefully he put it on the side of his
desk, then took a letter from the top of a huge stack of
mail and began to read.

Railey smiled and left. And Byrd tore into the backlog
of work. He answered his overdue correspondence and
burned the telephone lines putting through orders, prod-
ding, checking—marshaling his expedition forces into a
smooth-working team. When he stood up from his desk
that night, he was tired but almost happy again. "You're

127

coming to Antarctica with me, Floyd," he murmured. "We'll christen the Ford plane *Floyd Bennett.*"

Summer came and the long tedious preparations were almost completed. On August 25 the *City of New York* chugged out of New York harbor and set course for the Panama Canal and New Zealand. Almost a month later the *Eleanor Bolling*, named after Byrd's mother, followed in the *City*'s wake, heading for Norfolk, Virginia, where she took on stores already assembled on the quayside. And on September 30 Byrd closed his New York headquarters and went home to Boston to spend a few days with his family before his long trek south.

Byrd sat alone in his study, soaking up the quiet comfort of his home, listening to the faint sounds of the household in its daily routine. He could hear his three daughters and his son, Dickie, arguing about something upstairs; then there were footsteps and a timid knock on the door.

Eight-year-old Dickie came in. "Daddy, I have something for you," he said gravely. "I heard you say to Mother that you didn't have enough money for the expedition. I . . . well . . ." His little face reddened as he clutched something in his hand. "Here, Daddy, take this." The boy put a few crumpled dollar bills and some change on his father's desk. "I earned this last summer—four dollars and thirty-five cents."

Byrd hugged his son. "Dickie, this is going to help an awful lot. It will pay for food for the Huskies, or for gasoline for one of our planes." He cleared his throat. "On behalf of the entire expedition, I thank you."

The boy freed himself from his father's embrace. "I'll make some more, Daddy, and I'll send it to you," he said resolutely. "And I'll help Mother all I can while you're gone. I'm strong—see?" He stuck his chest out. "I'll be ten when you get back."

"Yes, you'll be half of twenty."

After the much-too-brief rest at home, Byrd, accompanied by his wife Marie, took the train for San Pedro, California, to board the *C. A. Larsen*. And on October 9 he waved the final good-bye to Marie as the *Larsen*'s powerful engines inched the ship away from the wharf.

With the crated aircraft, gasoline, and some one hundred tons of supplies on board, the *Larsen* headed for the rendezvous with the other ships of the expedition in Wellington, New Zealand. Two thousand miles south of Wellington lay Antarctica—five million square miles of unexplored territory.

In the cabin Byrd and Bernt Balchen, who had taken Bennett's place as the head of the expedition's "air force," held final conferences. The aircraft and the supplies would have to be unloaded from the *Larsen* and shipped to Antarctica piecemeal by Byrd's own two vessels. Captain Nielsen, the skipper of the *Larsen*, was anxious to start hunting for whales in the antarctic waters and the best he could do was to cut the way for Byrd's ships through the treacherous ice pack that barred access to the planned landing spot in the Bay of Whales.

During one of such planning conferences Captain Nielsen cleared his throat and said, "Today is October 25, 1928, according to my calendar. Does this date mean anything to any of you, gentlemen?"

Byrd and Balchen, engrossed in calculations, paid no attention. Nielsen reached into the cabin's closet and pulled out a small flat package. "Here, my friend," he said, handing the parcel to Byrd. "This is for you. Your wife gave it to me before we sailed. Happy birthday to you!"

Byrd arched his eyebrows in surprise. "But she already did give me my present!" He carefully unwrapped the gift—four birthday cards obviously created by his children: Dickie, Evelyn, Katherine, and baby Helen. "This is about the nicest way to be reminded of one's old age," Byrd said, chuckling. "Yes, gentlemen, having been born in 1880 *anno domini*, I am forty years old today."

"Ach, you don't look it, man," Captain Nielsen said.

"Well, I certainly don't feel it—especially in such good company as yours."

The reloading of the cargo onto the *City of New York* took almost a month. Meanwhile the *Larsen* had left for the hunting grounds. On or about December 10 the *Larsen* would meet the *City of New York* on the edge of the pack and serve as an icebreaker.

On December 2, 1928, the *City* cast off and, loaded to capacity, followed the *Bolling* south. On this trip the *Bolling* carried only extra coal, acting as a mother ship and a sea tug for the slower *City*.

With all her sails set and under steam, the *City* made about eight knots under the *Bolling*'s tow. Below decks every inch of space was crammed with gear and equipment. In fact, the cargo overflowed to the deck. Crates of food, the crated Fairchild aircraft, and the dog kennels were lashed down, leaving hardly room enough for the crew.

As the convoy plowed through the long swells, the sky became smoky-blue . . . then, gradually, gray patches darkened the blue in a confused pattern. Sverre Strome, a Norwegian ice pilot, studied those changes—the telltale signs of the nearness of the ice pack.

Breathing clouds of vapor, Sverre peered ahead from the lookout's barrel on the masthead. "Ice-ho!" he called. Byrd and his men ran on deck, crowding the ship's rail. As far as they could see from port to starboard, the thin white line of an enormous ice floe barred the way. Hanging above it like gray, wispy eyebrows, a snow cloud frowned at the daring intruders.

Snow squalls whitened the ocean, shrinking the visibility to the danger point. At times the *Bolling*'s black silhouette disappeared from view and only the tow line, taut under strain, told the *City*'s skipper that the tug was still ahead.

During one of those sudden squalls the *Bolling* stopped short, apparently to avoid running into a flat iceberg. The only warning to the *City*'s skipper was the slack in the tow cable. "Full astern!"

The *City*'s propeller reversed its beat, sending a shiver through the hull. The vessel slowed down and came to a stop just as the stern of the *Bolling* hove into view. Without warning the *Bolling* surged ahead. The steel cable hissed out of the water, twanged like a bass-fiddle string, and snapped. The cable winch spun crazily, unwinding the broken cable—and the *City* was on her own.

It was getting dark, and trying to repair the cable at night was hopeless. But Sverre Strome triumphantly boomed from the masthead, "*Larsen* dead ahead!" Under her own steam the *City* groped among the ice floes and by nightfall she and the *Bolling* were hugging the giant hull of the *Larsen* in a safe anchorage.

131

Now all the spare coal was transferred from the *Bolling* to the *City*. While the *Larsen*, with the *City* in tow, nosed into the thickening ice pack, the more fragile *Bolling* returned to New Zealand to take on more supplies and equipment.

Thirty-five times the size of the *City*, the *Larsen* nudged the ice mass, plowed it aside with a rumble, and shoved her steel bow into the opening like a wedge. At the end of her steel tow the *City* trailed cautiously, side-stepping the disturbed, precariously balanced giant slabs of ice. The *City's* wake of open water closed under the ice pressure. It narrowed into an almost-black line which finally disappeared like the erratic doodle of a pen that had suddenly run out of ink.

For twelve days and nights the ice pack reluctantly opened ahead of the *Larsen* and quickly closed astern of the *City* as though anxious to erase her wake. At last the lookout called, "Open sea ahead!" Gradually the ice turned to a soft mush. The black line on the horizon grew larger and, on December 23, the dark water of the Ross Sea gurgled merrily under the *City's* bow as the *Larsen* picked up speed.

Now the two ships parted company. The *Larsen* turned back north after whales and the *City* sailed toward the Ross Ice Barrier. On Christmas Day, Byrd stood on the bridge with Bernt Balchen. "Look, Bernt—the Barrier blink!" Byrd pointed ahead.

The "blink"—a slight brightening of the sky—was the sure sign of the huge icecap that stretched from the South Pole toward the Ross Sea.

The *City* reached the Barrier and cautiously cruised alongside, heading east, toward the Bay of Whales. The antarctic summer sun painted unexpected color into the awesome Barrier. The sea that washed the ice wall was inky black, with touches of sepia in the troughs of the waves. Gray-edged, jagged crevasses and bizarre caves gradually darkened into royal blue as they lured the eye into their mysterious depths. A sheared surface momentarily glared with molten-silver brightness, only to give way to a dark, ominous shadow as the ship slid past a tall ice bastion.

And the icescape changed with every turn of the *City*'s tired propeller. Now you could look over the Barrier's edge toward the olive-green clouds on the horizon; now the edge loomed high over the ship, chilling you with its icy breath.

Seemingly dead in its permanency, the Barrier was alive with distant rumbles and an occasional boom as loud as a thunderclap. It was the sound of battle between the ocean and the ice. Pounding furiously in a frontal attack or pushing invisibly with the subversive might of the long swells, the sea worked away at the Barrier. It cracked the glacier, tore off icebergs and sucked them away. Yet imperceptibly the billions of tons of ice crept seaward, closing the ranks, defiant and invincible—always there.

Byrd and the rest of his crew stood on the deck and watched the wild, bewildering beauty of the Barrier. "What a Christmas gift!" Byrd said, half to himself, half to Bernt Balchen.

Bernt lifted his eyebrows quizzically.

"It's Christmas Day, Bernt."

"*Ja*, it's Christmas," Bernt sighed.

On January 1, 1929, the *City* reached a low spot in

the Barrier—no more than thirty feet above the sea level. There the crew jumped ashore and drove the "dead men" —the ice anchors—into the bay ice. Tied to those anchors, the *City* lazily scratched her water-logged hull against the sharp ice edge as Byrd and Balchen led two dog teams in search of a suitable site on which to build a winter base.

Following an ice inlet, Byrd arrived in a flat hollow with gentle slopes—an excellent location for the base. "Well, here it is," he said, looking around. "This is where we're going to settle our Little America."

"Looks good, Dick," Bernt agreed.

Back at the *City*, they ran planks from the deck to the bay ice. Scientists and sailors alike carried crates of supplies, rolled drums of fuel oil and gasoline. The equipment and supplies were loaded on sledges which, pulled by five teams of eager Malemutes, shuttled between the ship and Little America.

First the men put up several tents. Then came the prefabricated wooden houses, and Little America slowly became a full-fledged base. Supplies were carefully sorted and neatly stacked. Radio masts were erected. Men were assigned to their quarters and, under Balchen's direction, the aviation group began reassembling the small Fairchild aircraft.

By the end of January the plane was flight-tested and Byrd decided to start preliminary exploration by air. On the first clear day, with Balchen and Hal June, he climbed into the small aircraft, took off, and set course for Scott's Nunataks—a patch of bare rock two hundred miles east of Little America.

Within an hour and forty-five minutes the plane

reached the dark-brown patch against the endless whiteness below. Byrd watched it with elation. What had taken Robert F. Scott many arduous weeks during his expedition of 1902, was now an easy, comfortable two-hour journey. Byrd looked at the plane's wing and thought of the mysterious aerodynamic forces harnessed by man—the weight of the aircraft balanced so perfectly by the pull of the propeller and the invisible life. By this magic of flight, he and his companions were able to explore four thousand miles of virgin frozen land every hour. . . .

The sharp contours of the terrain blurred in a thick grayish haze. Balchen pointed ahead and Byrd was able to read his lips. Storm!

The horizon began to close on the aircraft; then the air whitened with swirling snow. The dry, sharp snow crystals whispered against the windshield and the fuselage, lending a strange muffled quality to the engine's roar. Gradually the horizon, the ground below, and the blue sky merged into a darkening whiteness.

Balchen focused on the flight instruments. His gloved hands gently nudged the controls this way and that— holding a steady altitude, level and on course.

Hal June put his hands to his headset, frowned, then smiled. In large block letters he scribbled a radio message on his pad: BOLLING SIGHTED FROM LITTLE AMERICA.

Byrd read it and grinned. Time to turn back. He squinted out the window, searching the whiteness for a lighter patch—better weather. There it was—off the starboard wing tip—a blurred outline of the low, antarctic sun. "Turn ninety degrees right—head south," Byrd wrote and held the pad for Balchen to see.

In a few minutes they shot out of the snowstorm. Ahead, sharply silhouetted against the blue sky, was a mountain peak, then another and another.

"Our first discovery!" Byrd said excitedly, his words smothered by the engine roar. "Twelve, thirteen, fourteen peaks," he counted.

They flew along the crescent range, which now and then surprised them with bare, dark brown faces of rock scarred by untold ages of antarctic storms.

Balchen tapped the fuel gauge. Clumsily holding a pencil in his gloved fingers, he wrote, "Fuel running low."

Byrd nodded and gave the signal to turn for Little America.

The mountain towers swung behind. As though hypnotized by their rugged beauty Byrd swiveled his head, watching them until they melted in the smoky haze of the horizon. What shall we name them, he thought. Names of several friends came to his mind, but foremost among them was John D. Rockefeller, Jr. Byrd recalled the times of trouble in planning his first North Pole expedition; the flight to Paris; and this, the antarctic trip. And he remembered the astute advice and help the young Rockefeller had always given him.

Just before the plane circled the Little America landing field, he scribbled on his chart, "Rockefeller Mountains."

13 ☆

THE ANTARCTIC SUMMER HAD DISPERSED THE ICE PACK and now the *Bolling* was steaming to a landing. The flat bay ice crunched under the ship's steel bow and she finally made fast some fifty feet from the Barrier's icy cliff.

Scientists, airmen, and sailors joined forces to unload the *Bolling* so that she could make another supply run to Dunedin before the winter barred the approaches to Little America. The Ford and the Fokker planes were carted to their site for reassembly. The dog teams strained under the heavily loaded sledges, bringing more food, fuel, and equipment for the Ice Party—the forty-two men who were to stay at Little America.

One evening Byrd was on board the *City* discussing the time of the ship's departure when a thunderous roar rattled the cups on the cabin table. The *City* groaned and heeled over. The dishes slid from the table and crashed to the floor.

Byrd scrambled on deck. Against a cloud of pulverized ice the *Bolling* rolled to one side, exposing her rusty keel. Tons of ice broken off the Barrier cascaded onto the *Bolling*'s deck. Under the enormous weight the ship toppled—her masts touched the ice cliff, and the lines which tied her to the *City* creaked under a mighty strain.

Benny Roth, one of the mechanics, lost his footing on the slanting deck and fell into the sea among the madly swirling ice cakes. Commander Byrd acted by reflex. As he slid toward the taffrail he was tearing off his coat—getting ready to dive after the drowning man. Several of the crew grabbed him. A few minutes in the icy brine would mean sure death from exposure.

But Byrd brushed them aside. "Benny can't swim! Let go of me!" He dived into the sea and, clawing his way through the ice litter, swam toward the victim with powerful strokes.

Meanwhile a boat was lowered. It reached the scene as Byrd started towing the semiconscious man to safety. Both were hoisted on board the *City*, taken below, stripped, and rubbed down with brandy.

The ice was shoveled off the *Bolling*. She slowly righted herself and so did the *City*. Byrd, wrapped in a blanket and sipping hot tea, resumed his conference.

Dr. Lawrence Gould, second in command of the expedition, reproached Byrd for his rescue. "You shouldn't have done it, Dick. You're the leader of the expedition."

Byrd fixed him with his blue-gray stare. "I know, Larry. That's exactly why I jumped after the man," he said evenly. "As a leader I am responsible for his life."

138

Toward the end of February both ships were unloaded. The *Bolling* steamed out first. The delay in unloading made it too dangerous for the *Bolling* to attempt another run; so, rather than risk her safety, Byrd ordered the skipper to stay in New Zealand until the next antarctic summer. Following the *Bolling*, the *City* cast off and soon disappeared in a dense wisp of sea smoke. The forty-two inhabitants of Little America were left to their own resources with their radio as the only link with the outside world thousands of miles away.

Before burying the aircraft in their ice hangers for the long winter, Byrd decided to run one last exploration of the newly discovered Rockefeller Mountains. On March 7 Dr. Gould, Balchen, and June climbed into the Fokker and took off, planning to investigate the geology of the mountains for several days.

Four days later Gould radioed that the weather in the mountains had deteriorated and that his party would cut short the exploration. However, within an hour, he sent another message: "Take-off impossible due to storm."

Little America was also battered by a gale. Byrd camped by the radio desk as the radioman sent message after message to Gould. When there was no answer for three days, Byrd called in Dean Smith, another pilot of the expedition. "I'm sure something has gone wrong with Bernt and Larry," he said. "The winter night is too close to fool around—we'll have to run a rescue flight to the mountains as soon as the weather lets up."

Five more stormy days went by and Byrd was beside himself with worry. Finally, on March 19, the gale abated. Shielding their faces against the stiff breeze, at ten degrees below zero, Byrd, Smith, and a radio operator plodded to the Fairchild plane.

The Little America runway was crisscrossed with sastrugi—long patches of drift snow beaten into hard ice by the gale. The Fairchild started its take-off run. Its skis thumped on the sastrugi. The small plane rattled as though it were going to fall apart but, helped by a gust of wind, it took off.

Within an hour Byrd sighted the mountains. A few minutes later the plane reached the area where Larry Gould was supposed to have set up his camp. But there was no trace of the Fokker.

The winter dusk dimmed the vision. The Fairchild was wheeling around for the second survey when Byrd spotted a flashing light in the distance. "There!" he shouted over the engine's roar.

The plane thudded on the landing run and came to a stop in a snowdrift. Byrd jumped out. Running to meet him was Hal June . . . then Balchen, and Gould.

Laughing with joy, Byrd embraced each of them in turn. Then he pulled his sleeping bag out of the Fairchild and carried it several paces away from the group. He spread it on the frozen snow, knelt on it, and whispered a prayer of thanks.

With the night fast approaching there was no time for lengthy explanations. Balchen and June were ordered into the waiting Fairchild. Gould, Byrd and his radio operator waved the plane off and ran for the tent.

That night, snug in his sleeping bag, Byrd listened to Larry Gould's story. After the last radio message, a storm bore down on the expedition's camp. Winds up to 150 miles an hour lifted the anchored Fokker, flew the plane backward for half a mile, and smashed it against the ice. The crank of Gould's radio transmitter broke off and they could only listen to the messages from Little America but could not reply.

"We didn't worry too much," Gould said. "We knew you would come."

Byrd lay silent for a moment, thinking about the days and nights of his anxious vigil by the radio receivers. Then he said, "Of course, Larry. God's been good to us."

In two days the Fairchild plane completed the rescue and the Ice Party settled down for the four long months of winter. The buildings of Little America were connected with tunnels hacked in the ice. Above, vicious gales chased one another in the subzero darkness. Safely buried under the surface, the men worked out the details of the forthcoming tasks—the exploration of the Queen Maud mountain range and the flight to the South Pole.

Before the Queen Maud party of six men and four dog teams started south, a support party broke the trail and marked it with strips of bright cloth tied to bamboo splints which they stuck in the snow. Laden with food and supplies, these pathfinders established depots along the trail—thus enabling the main exploratory party to travel light and fast.

Byrd had planned the surface exploration, applying every bit of knowledge gained from his studies of the great polar explorers—Nansen, Shackleton, Scott, and Amundsen. To that knowledge he added his own experience. For example, the main item of the antarctic diet was pemmican—the traditional polar food. The meat was dried and pounded into half-pound blocks according to Amundsen's own formula. But Byrd wisely supplemented the pemmican rations with vitamin-giving powdered fruit.

With both surface parties off, Byrd began the final preparations for his long flight south. The tri-motor Ford, *Floyd Bennett*, was hauled to the surface from its winter ice hanger, inspected, and test-flown to double-check its fuel consumption. Then the cabin was loaded with three hundred pounds of food, two hundred gallons of gasoline, oil and a large stove for warming up the engines. These supplies were flown 450 miles south to the mouth of the Axel Heiberg Glacier, where Byrd established his only emergency depot for his subsequent polar flight.

On Thanksgiving Day, 1929, the Queen Maud party, already far along its trail, radioed that the weather there was perfect. "Cyclone" Haines, the chief meteorologist of Little America, confirmed a good-weather forecast. The *Floyd Bennett* was carefully loaded according to plan—extra gasoline in five-gallon cans, emergency rations, skis, tents, and sleeping bags—fifteen thousand pounds in all.

Balchen climbed into the pilot's seat; Hal June sat on his right as a copilot and radio operator. Ashley McKinley gingerly carried his cameras on board—he would provide a pictorial record of the land below. Last to board the plane was Byrd. Under his fur coat he carried a United States flag to be dropped on the South Pole. During the winter months Byrd had fastened a stone from Floyd Bennett's grave to the flag, using Floyd's worn flying scarf.

Balchen checked the engine gauges—the oil was warm; the three engines idled impatiently, belching black smoke from their exhaust stacks. "All set!"

Byrd gave the signal. Responding to the throttles, the engines revved up and sent a whirlwind of snow along the fuselage. The plane's skis creaked as the machine began to move, then thumped on the ice runway . . . faster, faster. A nervous shiver ran through the aircraft, vibrating the chronometers, maps, and sextant on Byrd's navigation table.

At 3:29 P.M. the ski shudder gave way to the undisturbed harmony of the engines as the *Floyd Bennett* left the ground.

At 8:15 P.M. Balchen pointed below. Byrd looked down. Against the vast whiteness they saw a small cluster of black specks like ants crawling over cottage cheese— the Queen Maud party.

Balchen swooped down on them as McKinley opened the trap door to jettison supplies they had requested by radio. Within seconds the party disappeared under the plane's tail.

Byrd thought of Amundsen and his long trek to the Pole, and his average speed of twenty miles a day. Now the *Floyd Bennett* was carrying the explorers along Amundsen's route at almost one hundred miles an hour. And, better, much faster aircraft were coming—to make future exploration even faster and safer. . . .

Safer? Byrd's precise mind visualized the plane's fragile fuel system—gasoline lines studded with fittings, each of which could spring a leak and drain precious fuel. And suppose there was a bit of dirt in the gas lines—it could plug one of the carburetor's jets; cause loss of power, perhaps engine stoppage. Could they maintain steady climb on two engines?

The altimeter wound up slowly. Three thousand feet,

four thousand . . . Still a long way to the eleven thousand they must have to clear the highest point of the Axel Heiberg Glacier—one of the gateways to the polar plateau. Will the three engines burn enough fuel to lighten the plane in time for that crucial climb?

From his base-laying flight to the mouth of the Axel Heiberg Glacier, Byrd knew that the cold air from the Pole poured down the sloping glacier and held back a climbing aircraft—trying to blow it down.

At 9:15 P.M. Byrd marked the aircraft's position on the chart and walked forward. Leaning over Balchen's shoulder, he peered ahead at the "Hump"—the jagged edge of the polar plateau. There was the familiar Heiberg glacier, disgorging a rippled river of ice.

Altitude? The altimeter needle quivered at nine thousand feet.

Balchen pointed to the Heiberg pass. A layer of cloud, gray on the bottom and silvery white on top, covered the pass like a thick, fuzzy blanket. It extended to the right, almost to the edge of the Liv Glacier—the alternate pass through the "Hump."

The *Floyd Bennett* droned on the original course. Balchen waited for Byrd's decision.

The altitude of the Liv Glacier was unknown. What if it proved too high for the plane's already straining engines? Yet it was the only way open to the Pole. Byrd swallowed hard. His hand felt as though it weighed a ton as he pointed the direction.

Obediently the aircraft nose pointed at the narrow mouth of the Liv passage. The frozen cascades of ice, rippled like a washboard and cracked by gaping crevas-

144

ses, ascended steeply. On the left Nansen Mountain towered over the climbing aircraft, and on the right the jagged peak of Fisher Mountain crowded the horizon. The center of the pass was studded with snow-covered islands of rock. A forced landing now would mean certain death.

As the *Floyd Bennett* winged into the pass, the polar down-draft slammed the plane with a barrage of punches. Balchen drew in his muscular neck and tightened his lips, getting ready for a fight. He nudged the throttles forward. The engines raised their pitch and the plane kept climbing.

Byrd planted his feet firmly against the cabin floor. His hands gripped the back of the pilot's seat. Leaning forward, he watched the climbing slope of the glacier—glancing from time to time at the rocky walls of the gorge that seemed to touch each wing tip. Too late to turn back—no room for maneuvering. His lips moved, breathing out wisps of vapor. "Climb, *Bennett*, climb."

The pointer of the altimeter wavered—the load of the plane was too much for the straining engines and the *Floyd Bennett* climbed no more. Shuddering with every gust of turbulent air, the plane slowly converged with the sloping glacier which rose to bar the flight path.

Hal June put his hand on the gasoline-dump valve. A slight pressure on that valve would spill hundreds of gallons of the precious fuel in seconds. McKinley dragged a large bag of emergency food to the trap door. The load had to be lightened were the aircraft to climb.

Which would it be—fuel or food? The split second of decision seemed like an hour to Byrd. He held back

145

June's hand and motioned to McKinley. The 125-pound bag of food went overboard.

The plane resumed its climb, then flattened out again —protesting with the desperate roar of its engines.

"More!" Bernt shouted. "She won't climb!"

The deadly ripples of the glacier were closing in fast.

Byrd's mind worked as rapidly as a whirling propeller. One bag of food, enough to feed his flight crew for two weeks in case of—

"Dump!"

Another bag went down.

As though surprised by this waste of life-giving food, the aircraft hesitated. The glistening mass of ice vanished under the plane's nose.

The freezing air burned in his lungs. Byrd braced himself for the crash.

Suddenly the plane leaped up. The black rocks of the mountains flanking the glacier sank under the wing tips. The *Floyd Bennett* cleared the "Hump" with only inches to spare and leveled out over the polar plateau.

Weak-kneed, Byrd walked back to his navigation table. His altimeter stood at eleven thousand feet. The chronometer ticked past 9:15 P.M.

Now Byrd worked like a machine. He sighted the sastrugi on the plateau below to determine the drift and the ground speed. With his sextant he "shot" the position of the sun, then checked the plane's progress toward the Pole against his dead-reckoning calculations. His mittened fingers, cramped from the subzero cold, could hardly hold the pencil. He corrected courses, checked and double-checked his figures.

The Queen Maud peaks melted in the hazy distance behind the plane. The South Pole—that imaginary point on the bottom of the world—was in sight.

Relieved by June at the controls, Balchen walked to Byrd's table. "Heavy clouds ahead," he wrote on the pad. "Looks like a storm."

Byrd studied the thickening haze and the low clouds that reached for the disk of the sun, which hung only a hand's breadth above the horizon. Trying to negotiate the Liv Glacier on the way back in the storm would be suicide, and so would be an attempted landing on the sastrugi-ridged ice mass of the plateau. If they turned back at once, the plane was sure to outrace the storm.

Byrd bent over his table and calculated the speeds. Then he wrote: "We are only thirty minutes from the Pole. Let's try for it!"

Balchen nodded and returned to the cockpit.

At 1:14 A.M. Greenwich mean time Byrd put down his sun compass and wrote excitedly: "We have just reached the South Pole!" He passed the note to Balchen.

The plane flew on, then doubled back. Byrd opened the trap door. Within a few seconds he would be staring at the South Pole directly below him. He reached for the stone fastened to the American flag. His lips, numb from cold, moved silently as he dropped the stone and flag through the door. Reluctantly he closed the hatch and gave the signal to turn back for Little America.

Still crouching over the closed trap door, Byrd thought of another flight—the trip "around the world" he and Bennett had made over the North Pole years ago. Then he gently patted the cabin wall. "Well, Floyd, old friend,"

147

he said, "we've made it again." He stood up. A tear shimmered in the corner of his eye. He shook his head and the tear fell, turning into a droplet of ice before it reached the cabin floor.

The *Floyd Bennett's* engines droned happily in a mighty chord.

14

BACK FROM THEIR EIGHTEEN-HOUR FLIGHT, THE CREW of the *Floyd Bennett* climbed down at Little America's landing strip. Stiff from cold and fatigue but jubilant, the four aerial explorers all talked at once, reliving their experiences for the benefit of those who had stayed behind.

That night, sitting by an oil lamp, Byrd made another entry in his diary: "Well, it's done. We have seen the Pole. McKinley, Balchen, and June have delivered the goods. They took the Pole in their stride, neatly, expeditiously, and undismayed. If I had searched the world I doubt if I could have found a better team. Theirs was the actual doing. But there is not a man in this camp who did not assist in the preparation for this flight. Whatever merit accrues to the accomplishment must be shared with them."

Byrd closed the bound copybook. With the roar of the *Floyd Bennett*'s engines still ringing in his ears, he slid into his sleeping bag. Before he let himself fall asleep, he took stock of the expedition's task. The Geological Party had radioed they were ready to return. The ground survey of the Bay of Whales was almost completed. The only thing left was an air exploration of the new land to the east. . . .

It took a few days to inspect the *Floyd Bennett*'s engines. But at ten minutes to eleven on the morning of December 5 Byrd gave the signal to take off.

For almost two hours they flew eastward over familiar territory. Then, with the Rockefeller Mountains well astern, the *Floyd Bennett*'s angular shadow raced over frozen land, unseen before and unclaimed.

According to leading geographers and geologists, Antarctica was not one continent but two. And just about here, Byrd thought, there should be the mysterious breach. . . . Carefully he scanned sastrugi and crevasses below, but he could see no sign of a split. The same solid land mass extended eastward to where, barely visible in the haze, a mountain range upset the smoothness of the horizon with saw-toothed peaks.

Now it was 1:30 P.M. As far as the eye could see, the steel-gray mountains ran from north to south. Behind the summits an endless plateau stretched—serene and mysterious.

The *Floyd Bennett* turned north, parallel to the range. Then, upon a signal from Byrd, the plane gently turned toward the mountains and back-tracked, stretching its right wing tip as though to touch the gray and white walls.

150

McKinley's camera clicked picture after picture, recording the new discovery until Byrd checked the fuel gauges. "Time to start for home," he wrote on the message pad.

"The flight to the eastward was more successful than I had dared to hope," Byrd recorded in his diary. "From a geological point of view, it proved the existence of land in that area. . . .

"The survey photographs which McKinley made will be interesting and important to glaciologists fifty and one hundred years from now, for they are a permanent record of ice conditions in 1929.

"To the new land I have given the name of Marie Byrd Land—after my wife, who has backed and helped me every foot of the way, who has shouldered much of the burden of the expedition, and whose understanding has made my many expeditions possible."

With the Geological Party back from their long trip south, the men of Little America started to pack the equipment and count the days till the arrival of the *City* and the homebound voyage.

On February 18 Captain Melville, the skipper of the *City of New York*, radioed that his ship was approaching Floyd Bennett Harbor. The population of Little America started its exodus. Cracking jokes and laughing, the men fell into the long line of sledges. Even the Huskies caught the joyful spirit. Barking and yelping, they pulled their heavy loads faster than ever before.

Byrd and Bill Haines, the expedition's meteorologist, made the final inspection of the abandoned camp. With the crew already gone, the mess hall built from dog crates, the "administration" building, and even the radio

151

towers assumed an air of strangeness. Little America was a ghost town.

The *Floyd Bennett* and the *Stars and Stripes*, firmly anchored by the mechanics, stood guard over the camp as though loath to leave the scene of their heroic conquest. The breeze tugged at their wings and enlivened them with impatient jerks against the mooring lines.

Byrd returned for a final farewell. "We'll be back," he said. Then he waved to the aircraft and followed the trail to the harbor.

He started planning his second antarctic expedition on the way home from the first. The Marie Byrd Land region had to be explored by a ground party. Also the vast territory of the interior, south of Little America, would have to be mapped and investigated more thoroughly. Then, of course, the studies of the antarctic weather must be continued, possibly through the long polar winter.

Discussing his still-vague plans, Byrd said, "If I live to be a hundred, I won't have enough time to explore those five million square miles. For all we know, there may be immense mineral wealth to be found and tapped. We have only begun the enormous task of exploring that new continent."

Paul Siple, an Eagle Scout and the youngest member of the expedition, raised his hand. "Sir, shouldn't the U. S. Government get interested in the antarctic exploration?"

Byrd nodded thoughtfully. "Yes, I think so. But first we and our supporters, the private citizens, should lay the groundwork. It's up to us to prove to the American people that their government should look into the matter."

152

However, when Byrd landed in the United States the country was in the throes of depression and even private support for another expedition was hard to find. The United States Congress promoted Byrd to the rank of Rear Admiral, and a special Congressional Medal was struck to be presented to all members of his expedition. Yet few people listened to Byrd's appeal for funds.

He wrote articles, lectured from coast to coast, explaining the need for further work in the antarctic—needling, arguing, and almost begging.

"You should slow down, Dick," his brother Tom told him. "Look at you—if it weren't for your uniform, people would let you cut in at the front of any bread line. Why don't you rest —put some flesh on your bones?"

"I've got to go on with my plans," Byrd said. "I owe this effort to the Navy, the American people, and—who knows?—perhaps to the entire world."

"And suppose you don't get the necessary backing?"

Byrd looked at his brother and smiled. "Come now, Tom. You know me better than that," he said. "I'll get it."

It took him almost four years, but he did get it. The U. S. Shipping Board lent him an old steamer, which was rechristened *Jacob Ruppert*. With borrowed money Byrd bought a decrepit icebreaker, the *Bear*, from the city of Oakland, California. William Horlick's cash donation paid for a Curtiss-Wright Condor biplane powered by two engines.

Edsel Ford again came to the rescue—he gave two snowmobiles. The Cleveland Tractor Company presented Byrd with a Cletrac—a tracked vehicle which could carry a ten-ton load over the deepest snow. And, from

153

France, his old friend André Citroën sent three fast snow cars.

What Byrd could not raise from backers and contributors, he borrowed. On October 3, 1933, the *Ruppert* cast off from Newport News with aircraft, supplies, 153 dogs, and fifty-six explorers on board.

Fog and gales slowed down the southward voyage of 13,323 nautical miles. But on January 17, 1934, the *Ruppert* anchored some five hundred yards off the Barrier. Byrd, Bill Haines, and George Noville were with the scouting party that went ashore.

One of the three radio towers was leaning slightly, as though fatigued from bucking the antarctic gales. The "administration" building and the mess hall were buried under four feet of snow.

"The planes are gone!" Bill Haines pointed to the spot where the *Floyd Bennett* and the *Stars and Stripes* had been anchored.

Scanning the smooth snow hill, Byrd spotted the tip of a vertical stabilizer. Several feet away, an ice-glazed wing panel of the smaller plane blinked a welcome-home message in the arctic sun.

"The planes are safely buried there," Byrd said. "We'll dig them out later."

Meanwhile an excavation party was digging through the snow. In the mess hall they found frying pans on the stove still full of frozen food. They started a fire, warmed up the food and ate it with relish. Everything was perfectly preserved—even the whale meat and the beef in the supply tunnel were as good as when stored there four years before.

Byrd munched his whale steak thoughtfully. "You

know, this in itself is a great discovery," he said. "Maybe somebody will develop a way of preserving and storing fresh food in freezers someday. Perhaps years from now, Antarctica will become the world's natural cold storage for vast amounts of food so that nobody in the world will have to go hungry."

With the supplies unloaded and stored, the expedition began its exploratory work. One of the projects was to man an advanced weather base through the approaching winter months. The site selected was 123 miles south of Little America. Tractors and dog teams carried supplies and the sections of a prefabricated shack to be sunk in the snow.

Original plans called for a three-man crew to make weather observations regularly and radio the readings to the main camp. However, the tractors were breaking down in the subzero cold and it would be impossible to transport enough supplies to the advanced base before the arctic winter set in. Therefore only one man would be sent.

Byrd stayed up late that night discussing the situation with Bill Haines, the expedition's meteorologist. Study of the antarctic air masses, temperatures, wind directions and velocities was tremendously important. It would help toward better understanding of weather and be invaluable in forecasting, Haines explained.

"This being the case," Byrd said, "I am going to man the advanced base alone."

Haines protested. "Look, Dick, when I said it was important, I certainly didn't mean that you should risk your neck to get the data."

"I know, Bill. And, to put your mind at ease, I won't

155

be making a sacrifice for the sake of science. I am going to do it more for selfish reasons."

Haines raised his eyebrows.

Byrd went on. "Sure. There comes a time in every man's life when he should take stock of himself—sort of check on his navigation, so to speak." Byrd smoothed the chart on the table with the palm of his hand. "You see, it has taken me a long time to get where I am today. And we are all like aircraft on nonstop flights, with time like precious fuel which we cannot replenish. God alone knows how much time-fuel I have left, and I'd like to check my course—make sure that where I am headed is where I *should* be going. I can do it best alone—out there."

Haines nodded. "I think I understand. Well, best of luck, Dick. I'm going to turn in now."

After Haines left, Byrd wrote a special order for the men in Little America.

The following new appointments are made, to be effective during my absence:

Second in Command—Dr. Thomas C. Poulter
Third in Command —William Haines
Chief of Staff   —Harold June
Executive Officer   —George Noville

These officers will be obeyed and respected accordingly.

In the morning Byrd quickly packed a few of his belongings—books, phonograph records, a chronometer, a sextant, and a shaving kit. He shook hands with the men and climbed into the waiting plane. "See you next spring," he said, smiling.

156

An hour and ten minutes later, the plane swooped low over the advance-base site. Little black specks—the construction crew—waved an excited welcome.

The pilot circled the group, then leveled off for the landing. Byrd motioned to him to keep the engine revved up. Stopping or even slowing the engine at sixty degrees below zero would congeal the oil and make the restart a drawn-out affair.

The plane touched down. As the landing skis swooshed on the dry snow, Byrd tossed out his duffel bag and tumbled out after it. The plane picked up speed and took off again.

Byrd shook the snow from his parka hood and made his way to the construction group. "I see you haven't been wasting time getting the base in shape," he said happily. "Let me give you a hand!"

The prefabricated shack was sunk into the snow pit fifteen feet long, eleven wide, and eight deep. Thus buried, the hut would be safe from the winter gales and the snowdrifts which mounted rapidly around any exposed object.

Then Byrd and his men dug two tunnels in the ice— one for fuel and the other for food and miscellaneous supplies he would need throughout the lonely vigil. Paul Siple helped set up meteorological equipment in the instrument shelter on top—thermometers, a weather vane with a wind-speed indicator, and a hygrometer for measuring humidity.

The radio antenna was strung on two bamboo poles. The oil stove was connected and was soon burning merrily inside the shack. The construction crew hurriedly shoved the supplies into the tunnels and started preparations for their return trip to Little America.

The thermometer stood at sixty-four below zero. In the dusk of the approaching antarctic winter, fur-bundled men crouched in the snow, warming up their tractors' engines with blowtorches. Reluctantly the engines sputtered and started. "Keep them going," Byrd said. "If you let them stop, you might be here all winter!"

The men climbed onto their machines. Paul Siple turned back. "Careful with that stove, Admiral!" he called. "Remember to keep the ventilating pipe clear!" The gears ground and the tractors began to roll to the clatter of their caterpillar tracks, drowning the rest of Siple's message. All Byrd could make out was "fumes."

He watched the crawling machines from the top of his buried shack until the plumes of the exhaust vapor vanished in the dusk. Then he scanned the empty horizon and slowly went below.

Fumes, he thought. Ah, yes. He remembered when they were testing the oil stove back in Little America—the burner gave out lethal carbon monoxide. Poor Siple got quite ill. But afterward a new burner was made and it worked well.

He sniffed the air. It was heavy with the sickish smell of oil. Byrd took off his parka and hung it on a nail to thaw out. He checked the stovepipe and held his bare hand to the outlet of the ventilator duct. The stovepipe joints were a little loose-fitting, but the freezing fresh air came into the shack all right.

He turned off the stove oil, opened the door wide, then quickly undressed and slid into his sleeping bag.

Up at eight o'clock every day to take the weather

158

observations, Byrd filled his days with reading, listening to his phonograph records, meditating, and attending to various emergencies.

On March 29 he wrote in his diary: "Last night, when I finished writing, I noticed a dark patch spreading over the floor from under the stove. A bad leak had opened up in the fuel line. Worried about the fire risk, I shut off the stove and searched all through my gear for a spare line. I couldn't find one . . . but finally succeeded in stopping the leak with adhesive tape from the medical chest. Result: I was up until four o'clock this morning, most of the time darned cold, what with the fire out and the temperature inside the shack at fifty-eight degrees below zero. The cold metal stripped the flesh from three fingers of my hands."

Ten days passed. . . . The pressure gasoline lamp hung from the ceiling and cast a sharp cone of light, leaving the rest of the shack in semidarkness and giving an illusion of spaciousness. Byrd rubbed his fingers, numb from writing. He stood up to stretch, then by force of habit he held his hand to the ventilator outlet. There was no familiar bite of the freezing outside air.

Hurriedly he disassembled the ventilator pipe. It was clogged with ice. He put the pipe sections on the stove to thaw out.

"I am rather worried about the blockage," he wrote in his diary. "Unless the fumes from the stove escape to the surface, I shall have trouble."

The temperature dropped steadily for six days. The novocain ampules in Byrd's medical kit froze and shattered, as did the glass fire extinguishers. Two cases of tomato-juice bottles burst.

"Took my daily walk in eighty-nine degrees below zero," Byrd wrote on April 14. "Due west, Venus was an unblinking diamond set off exquisitely in the sea of blue. In the northeast, a silver-green serpentine aurora pulsed and quivered gently. In places, the Barrier's whiteness had the appearance of dull platinum. The colors were subdued; the jewels few; the setting simple. But the way these things went together showed a master's touch.

"I paused to listen to silence. My breath crystallized as it passed my cheeks. . . .

"Harmony—that was it! A gentle rhythm, the strain of a perfect chord; the music of spheres, perhaps.

"It was enough to catch that rhythm, momentarily to be myself a part of it. In that instant, I could feel no doubt of man's oneness with the universe. . . . It was a feeling that went to the heart of man's despair and found it groundless."

On May 26 the small gasoline engine for the radio-transmitter generator had to be thawed out by the stove before Byrd could start it. He carried the warmed-up engine to the food tunnel, connected the exhaust with the special ventilating pipe, and pulled the starting cord.

Leaving the rhythmic putt-putt behind, Byrd rushed to his radio table, eager to hear his friends' voices from Little America and to send his routine messages by Morse code. Laboriously he tapped out the message to Hal June and another to be transmitted from Little America to Boston—to Marie. . . .

He had tapped and listened in turn for over an hour when the generator engine began to sputter. "Wait," he tapped with his radio key.

160

The voice in the headset crackled: "Okay, Dick. Anything wrong?"

Byrd took off the headset and hurried to the tunnel. The air was thick with exhaust gases. He bent over the carburetor to adjust it. When he straightened up, the dark tunnel, the engine, and the patch of light from the shack whirled around him in a sickening spin.

He fell to the floor.

Out of the darkness came a voice like a warning cry muffled to a whisper by the roar of aircraft engines: "Get up, Dick . . . keep your head . . . crawl out of the tunnel."

The cold from the icy floor burned his cheek. He lifted his head. It weighed a ton . . . he let it drop again.

But the voice persisted. Was it Floyd? Tom?

He was in the garden, behind the house on Amherst Street. Tom's husky body pressed him down into the ground. He grasped for air. If he could only get his knee under Tom's belly . . .

"Give up?"

Straining painfully, Byrd brought his knee up and under his abdomen. With superhuman effort he straightened his arms . . . the other knee . . . On all fours he crawled toward the blurry patch of light.

The radio . . .

The radio table was higher than he could reach.

"Come on, Dick."

Panting, he reached for the radio key. "See . . . you . . ." His arm dropped. What was it he wanted to say? "Help"? The arm wasn't really so heavy once it started to lift. He finished tapping the message: ". . . Sunday."

He pulled the ignition switch and the engine's putt-putt stopped. But the roar in his ears persisted. It filled his

161

head with pulsating pain. Then, like hot sunlight focused by a magnifying glass into a burning point, the pain converged into a stabbing flame deep behind his eyes.

He dropped to the floor again. If he could only reach his sleeping bag . . . Groping in the freezing darkness, he inched toward the bunk. His outstretched hand felt the friendly touch of the wooden frame.

15

WHEN HE CAME TO, BYRD WAS IN HIS SLEEPING BAG. IN vain he tried to remember how he got into it. His mouth was parched, but he couldn't move to get himself a drink. However, the pain was gone and the sleep had restored the clarity of his thinking.

Obviously he had been poisoned by the carbon monoxide of the exhaust fumes and needed help—nursing care and rest. Yet, in the midst of the antarctic winter, he couldn't hope to be rescued by an expedition from Little America. Even the most experienced antarctic explorers would be risking death in the darkness on the crevasse-ridden trail. No, he would never ask his friends to undertake the trip.

Obviously he would have to nurse himself—do the necessary things slowly, with minimum effort. Of course this was almost hopeless. . . .

"Have faith," he whispered to himself. "You must go on and on—you're flying—you must trust your instruments. Whatever goes wrong will be of your own making."

"Have faith," he muttered. "All right. The first thing I need is food and drink . . . and warmth."

It took him hours to crawl out of his sleeping bag and dress. Bumping into the chair, desk, and walls, he finally made it to the stove. Matches. He turned on the valve, struck a match, and held the quivering flame to the burner. The oil caught and burned red and smoky.

He sat close to the stove, soaking up the warmth. There were a few slivers of ice in the bucket. He sucked on them until his teeth chattered.

Now the pain returned—behind the eyes and through his entire body. Groaning, he retreated to his bunk.

Exhausted from the effort, he slept fitfully—drifting into nightmares and waking to the relentless darkness. But when he could think again, he knew he would win the battle. His body still ached in every fiber, but he was determined to fight.

His fingers felt his diary lying on top of the bunk. He found a match and lighted a candle. His hand trembling, he wrote: "The universe is not dead. Therefore there is an Intelligence. . . . It has been called by many names. Many call it God." . . .

The pencil fell out of his numbed fingers and he lay back, gasping. Then he started to dress. Having faith in God was good, he reasoned, but it wasn't enough. He would have to work—meet Him halfway.

Day by day Byrd worked according to his simple schedule: getting food and drink, using the stove sparingly because of the fumes, and resting. Above all, he watched himself for any dark thoughts of despair.

"This form of mental discipline is toughest of all," he wrote. But he whipped himself to go on.

Soon he was able to reestablish radio contact with Little America. Careful not to alarm his friends, he limited his messages to a very few words—mostly weather observations.

"I am still in wretched condition," Byrd wrote on July 7. "For weeks I ran a high temperature. And now I am facing another illness with a weakened body and mind. . . .

"Today I missed another radio schedule with Little America. I called and listened for at least half an hour. Then I broadcast blind: 'Can't hear anything. Receiver out of order. O.K. here. O.K., O.K., O.K.' I was teetering on the thin edge of oblivion."

On July 15 Byrd gathered enough strength to crank his emergency generator by hand. After a long trial he made contact with Little America. Dr. Poulter was talking.

"We shall try to send a party to you earlier than originally planned," he said. "Following our start from here, light a can of gasoline on top as a beacon for us."

Two days later Little America sent a message that Dr. Poulter's expedition would set out that morning. Byrd crawled on top to set up his gasoline beacon.

On July 26, after a week of radio silence and hopeful vigil, Byrd received another message. Dr. Poulter's party had been forced to turn back by an antarctic hurricane.

Shivering from exhaustion, Byrd kept up his daily routine. He made his weather observation, maintained a radio-listening schedule, and dragged himself out of the

165

shack to look for the tractor's searchlights—in case Poulter had left Little America unannounced.

On August 4 a message came through. Poulter had left earlier that day, but was stuck in the crevasses less than ten miles out of Little America. The message trailed off into a crackling deluge of static.

Four days later Little America signaled Poulter's third try. "Keep the beacon lights going, Dick," the voice said. "This time I think they're going right through."

On August 11, a little after midnight, Byrd awoke with a start. "I must light up the signal," he muttered. He laboriously climbed through the roof hatch and fired a flare. He closed his eyes to avoid the fierce glare; but when he opened them again and looked to the north, he saw the long finger of a searchlight beam probing the darkness. Dr. Poulter's party had arrived.

Too weak to endure the surface trip to Little America, Byrd remained at the advanced base for two more months under Poulter's care. On October 14 the same aircraft that had dropped him off seven months before took him on board and flew him back.

"Part of me remained forever at Latitude 80 degrees 8 minutes South," Byrd wrote later. "On the other hand, I did take away something that I had not fully possessed before: appreciation of the sheer beauty and miracle of being alive, and a humble set of values."

Still confined to bed, Byrd directed the rest of the explorers' tasks until the *Ruppert* arrived at Floyd Bennett Harbor to take them home. Thus the expedition brought back to the States priceless aerial photographs of almost half a million square miles of virgin territory, plus invaluable weather data and meteorological studies done by Byrd himself before his illness.

On May 10, 1935, Byrd stepped ashore at the Washington Navy Yard. President Franklin D. Roosevelt came in person to greet the returning hero.

Byrd's white uniform still hung a little loosely, but he saluted smartly. "Mister President, I wish to report mission accomplished."

Roosevelt flashed a smile and shook Byrd's hand warmly. "You really had me worried when I found out about your ordeal," he said. "Are you all right, Dick?"

"Yes, sir. And I'll be ready to go back again soon. Only this time—"

"I know," Roosevelt interrupted. "This time you want government support." He put his arm around Byrd. "Well, if you are willing to risk your life for Antarctica, exploration of that continent must be worth-while. And the least the people of America can do is to make further explorations possible. I expect to have your proposal on that. Oh, and one thing more—from the heart. Dick, I salute you."

With this major victory accomplished, Byrd started laying plans for his next venture—a prolonged study of geology, biology, meteorology, and other scientific aspects of Antarctica.

Thus, in 1939 at the age of fifty-one, Byrd commanded the United States Antarctic Service expedition. Surface parties and aircraft explored and mapped another one hundred thousand square miles of the continent, returning to the States only when the World War II situation forced the President to call the expedition home.

Back on active naval duty, Byrd made the rounds of

the Pentagon, buttonholing his admiral-friends, asking them for a battle assignment. "Look, I missed all the action in the last war," he pleaded. "I'm a pretty good navigator. . . . How about putting me on one of your carriers?"

The answer was invariably, "Sorry, Dick, maybe a little later."

Then in May, 1942, Byrd was summoned to the White House. The President waved to him from his desk. "Good to see you again, Dick," he said. "Pull up a chair—this assignment is going to take some time to explain."

The assignment was just what Byrd was hoping for—finding bomber and naval bases in the South Pacific islands.

"It will probably be a little too warm for your liking," Roosevelt said. "But we need this information in a terrific hurry."

Byrd virtually flew back to his Pentagon office. "We're off at once, Ed," he said to his aide, Lieutenant Edward Sweeney. "We have lots to do."

The next day Byrd and Sweeney took off in a Pan American Clipper for Pearl Harbor. From there, they traveled by seaplane tender to Samoa, Fiji, New Hebrides, New Zealand, Tahiti, and back to San Francisco.

On the plane to Washington, Byrd reviewed his voluminous notes, sketches, and photographs. "I don't know what I would have done without you, Ed," he said. "You deserve a leave as soon as we get in."

"How about you, sir?" Sweeney said.

Byrd smiled. "Don't worry about me. Washington is a second home to me anyway."

Byrd had no sooner submitted his secret report than

President Roosevelt had another assignment for him. "The material you brought is excellent, Dick," he said. "What we need now is an air-supply route which would by-pass Pearl Harbor—a sort of back-door way to get to those advanced bases. It's up to you to map it out."

Again Byrd and Sweeney, with a group of fifteen experts, set out, this time on board a cruiser—the *USS Conqueror*. At their first stop—off Clipperton Island, some 670 miles southwest of Mexico—Byrd flew in the cruiser's seaplane to survey the terrain and choose an air-strip site.

There was no suitable harbor at Clipperton; so Byrd and his shore party had to reach the uninhabited island in the cruiser's launch, through a heavy surf. A giant breaker loomed off the bow. The helmsman did not turn into it in time and the breaker lifted the launch, almost capsizing it.

Thrown off balance, Byrd was momentarily suspended in the air. Then the boat lurched again and Byrd landed on his back with a dull thud.

"You all right, Admiral?" Ed Sweeney bent over him.

Byrd's face paled under the tan. Beads of perspiration glistened on his broad forehead. "I think so, Ed. Just help me up."

Byrd continued the survey, but every step he took was well-camouflaged agony. Sweeney suggested examination by the cruiser's doctor, but Byrd refused to listen. "They'd have me in a hospital before you could say 'medical officer.' It's just a bad sprain, that's all. And you must promise me not to breathe a word about it to anybody."

Sweeney kept his promise and Byrd completed his

169

report—five volumes with detailed description, maps, and photographs.

Byrd was still walking stiffly when his next assignment came—a secret study of how our air strategy should be shaped to prevent another surprise attack on the United States. Now he stayed at his Pentagon office late into the night, calculating and planning.

Once he telephoned Sweeney at two o'clock in the morning. "Ed, I've just finished the first draft of the concept and I want you to listen to it."

"Yes, sir."

Byrd expounded his theory of bases in Japan, Okinawa, and the Philippines. "If we maintain our striking air forces there, the Russians will not dare attack," he said.

Still groggy with sleep, Sweeney protested. "But, sir, I thought they were our allies—"

'They are," Byrd said. "But, after we defeat the Axis, Red Russia will be the only power left which could wage war on the United States."

Sweeney was silent and Byrd continued. "Of course, as long as we keep up our air strength in the Pacific and in Europe, they won't dare. We could use permanent peace in the world for a change. You know, Ed, if the military effort ever turned to exploration we could have peaceful international competition—we'd sort of let off steam in a constructive way. . . . You must go to Antarctica with me, Ed. Then, you'll see how much there's still to be done."

"I'd like that very much, sir."

"You know, maybe we could fly from the South Pole to the North Pole nonstop," Byrd chuckled. "Well, we'll see. Good night, Ed. I have to report to the President tomorrow—better get some sleep."

President Roosevelt's gaunt face lighted when Byrd reported to his office the next day. "We're running out of decorations for you, Dick," he said. "However, here is the Legion of Merit. You have done a grand job for the country."

Roosevelt leaned back in his chair. "I remember years ago, a young fellow, just back from the North Pole, came up the steps of the Capitol in Albany. . . . Well, do you think you've accomplished all you wanted to accomplish then, Dick?"

"Not quite, Franklin."

The President raised his eyebrows quizzically.

"As soon as the war is over," Byrd said, "I'd like to see a major effort in antarctic exploration—permanent bases down there, perhaps one right on the South Pole."

"I am sure the Navy can help you there."

"The Navy, the Air Force . . . other governments . . . There's so much to be learned at Antarctica."

"Well, Dick, you'd better get ready," Roosevelt said. "General Marshall tells me the war is not going to last much longer."

Eight months later, on September 2, 1945, Byrd was among the officers on board the *USS Missouri* witnessing the formal surrender of the defeated Japanese Empire. And he was ready and free to go south again.

16

A BATTLESHIP-GRAY NAVY JEEP BOUNCED ALONG THE
Tokyo streets. Sitting next to a helmeted driver, Admiral
Byrd absently returned salutes. His thoughts were thousands of miles away—in another hemisphere; another
world, untouched by the horror of nuclear blasts. Suddenly the driver slammed on the brakes to avoid a group
of Army men. Byrd looked up. Towering over the group
was a familiar figure. "Paul! Paul Siple!"

The tall Army major turned. "Admiral!"

The two men warmly shook hands. "What are you
doing in Japan, Paul?"

"Special mission—clothing and personal-equipment
study. And you?"

"I'm on my way to the States," Byrd said. "Have just
finished a report on the bombing survey of Hiroshima
and Nagasaki. Say, why don't you climb in and ride with
me to the airport? I don't want to miss my flight."

172

As they drove on, Byrd told Siple about his plans for another Antarctic expedition. "I broached the idea to Admiral Nimitz—an all-out peacetime attack on Antarctica: ships, planes, and men. He promised his full support. It's going to be the biggest expedition yet attempted. Care to come along?"

"I haven't missed one yet," Siple said, flashing a wide smile.

The jeep drove through the gate of Tachikawa airfield and stopped by a transport plane. Byrd jumped out. "So long, Paul. Hurry up with your work here and see me in Washington," he said, then turned to the driver. "Stay with Major Siple—take him wherever he wants to go."

A week later, in a Navy Department briefing room, Byrd unfolded his plan to Secretary of the Navy James Forrestal, Fleet Admiral Chester W. Nimitz, Vice Admiral Forrest P. Sherman, and a score of high-ranking government officials.

Pointing to the large wall map of Antarctica, Byrd said, "In effect, this would be a three-front attack on the continent. One group of three ships would move eastward from the ninetieth meridian and proceed as far as possible toward the meridian of Greenwich, east of the Weddell Sea.

"Another group would start from the Balleny Islands, south of New Zealand, and proceed westward until it meets the first group.

"Each of these groups would carry three PBM flying boats and their crews. The planes are to be launched from the open sea. They will photograph the coast and fly inland as far as possible.

"Between these two groups, there would operate the

173

Central Group with a base on the ice near the Bay of Whales. Its ski-equipped planes would fly over a sector of about eighty degrees in which lies the Ross Sea. Thus we would close a complete circle around the Antarctic continent."

Byrd turned his back on the map. Erect and trim, he appeared much younger than his fifty-seven years. His wavy hair, now almost white, created a startling contrast with his handsome face, still bronzed from the Pacific sun. As he paused for a deep breath his blue-gray eyes shifted from face to face, gauging the attention of his audience.

"Gentlemen," he said, "within a few weeks we hope to learn more of the great unknown, from this operation, than has been learned from a century of previous exploration by land and by sea."

Secretary Forrestal shifted in his chair. "How many ships will you need for this, Dick?"

"Thirteen, sir."

"And man power?"

"About four thousand men."

Forrestal nodded. "Fine. And when do you propose to start?"

"In December, 1946," Byrd said.

On December 2, 1946, the antarctic "armada" of OPERATION HIGHJUMP sailed from Norfolk, Virginia. And on January 29, 1947, Admiral Byrd climbed into the cockpit of an R4D on board the aircraft carrier *Philippine Sea*, steaming along eight hundred miles north of Little America.

Byrd gave a signal. Commander Bill Hawkes, the pilot, flipped the switch of the Jato rockets fastened under the plane's fuselage. The rockets roared and the plane blasted off the deck at full throttle, trailing white smoke. One after another, six R4D cargo planes took off and set course for Ross Barrier and the landing strip at Little America.

A few hours later Byrd was sipping hot coffee with Paul Siple in Little America's "veterans' tent," where twelve old-timers of Byrd's previous expeditions gathered daily. "To think that within the past few weeks aircraft have been discovering new land, mapping the coast line, and that ground parties have been conducting exploration—doing more in one hour than we accomplished in months," Byrd said.

"Yes, we've made considerable progress," Siple agreed. "What you have now is a fleet of ships and an air fleet to do the exploring."

Byrd nodded silently. He remembered a winter evening in New York before his first antarctic expedition. Floyd Bennett had spoken almost the same words over a cup of coffee. "It's more like commanding an army," Floyd had said. "You have an enemy—the antarctic weather and the five million square miles of that unknown continent."

Paul Siple went on. "Of course we need such an effort. There's still so much to learn. The entire area beyond the South Pole, for instance, is still a mystery. Incidentally, when are you going on your second flight to the Pole?"

"The Pole? Oh, yes. We'll go as soon as the weather conditions are right."

At 11:00 P.M. on February 15 two R4D planes roared down the ice runway at Little America on their way to

175

the unknown area beyond the South Pole. Riding in the cockpit of the lead plane was Admiral Byrd.

As the planes climbed on their course south, the temperature began to drop steadily. The cabin heater in Byrd's plane broke down and the windshield frosted up. Taking turns with the copilot, Byrd scraped the glass with a knife.

The plane's two engines harmonized in a powerful chord. Effortlessly the machine climbed over the "Hump" —the Queen Maud range which had almost succeeded in barring the *Floyd Bennett* from reaching the Pole almost seven years before.

Byrd glanced at his wrist watch. In twenty minutes they should be over the Pole. He went back to the navigator's station. Lieutenant (j.g.) Robert Heekin was taking his bubble sextant out of its plush-lined case.

"Know how to tell when we are *there*?" Byrd asked, smiling.

Heekin nodded. "Sure. When the altitude of the sun and the sun's declination are equal, sir."

Byrd smiled. "You don't mind if I do my own observations with the sun compass? It's not that I don't trust you, Bob."

"No, sir!"

At a signal from Byrd the plane banked, pointing one wing toward the antarctic sky and the other at a point twenty-five hundred feet below. At that point, buried under many feet of snow, was a stone with the United States flag and the flying scarf of Floyd Bennett.

The sun, low on the polar horizon, painted the snow with gold. Byrd slid open the cockpit window and tossed a small cardboard box into the howling slip stream outside. In the box were the flags of the United Nations.

The planes continued beyond the Pole into the "area of inaccessibility"—a flat, barren surface scarred with sastrugi. Then the radio crackled a message from Little America: "Suggest return as soon as possible. Weather is closing here."

In just over twelve hours of flight, the two R4D's slid to a stop on Little America's landing strip.

A week later Byrd ordered the evacuation of Little America and the return to the United States. During the few weeks of the exploration the planes of OPERATION HIGHJUMP had mapped an area more than half the size of the United States. More than fifty-four hundred miles of coast line were discovered or confirmed. Ten new mountains; new archipelagoes, seas, and ice-free regions were found and charted.

Standing in the stern of the *Mount Olympus*, Byrd and Paul Siple looked at the mighty Ross Barrier. While the throbbing engines urged the ship northward, the rugged wall of ice slowly fell away until it vanished in the descending dusk of the antarctic winter.

As they reluctantly went below, Byrd said, "There's still so much to be done here. Antarctica is a perfect laboratory for scientists of all nations working together. Perhaps out of their combined work—face to face with God—lasting world peace would evolve."

Siple was silent for a while, then said, "There could be permanent scientific stations in Antarctica—even one on the Pole." They stopped in front of Byrd's cabin. "You know," Siple continued softly, "ever since I helped build the advanced base for your stay in 1934 I've wanted to spend a winter in Antarctica—just as I've always wanted to go all the way to the Pole."

Byrd's blue-gray eyes rested on the young scientist's face. "Maybe you will, Paul," he said. "Maybe you will someday soon."

In 1952, when the International Council of Scientific Unions appointed a special committee for the International Geophysical Year, Byrd's reports and recommendations for an intensified study of Antarctica bore fruit. The giant scientific program in which sixty-four nations would participate included establishment of bases in Antarctica.

With renewed energy Byrd pleaded for another antarctic expedition. "We've led the world so far," he said. 'We certainly should make one more effort to pave the way for the International Geophysical Year."

On March 28, 1955, President Eisenhower announced that Rear Admiral Byrd would head a new United States antarctic expedition—OPERATION DEEPFREEZE—which would be responsible for the Antarctic phase of this nation's participation in the International Geophysical Year of 1957–59.

Byrd read the Presidential order: "Rear Admiral Richard Evelyn Byrd is designated Officer-in-Charge, United States Antarctic Programs. In this capacity, he shall act as senior U. S. representative in charge of those political, scientific, legislative and operational activities which comprise the total U. S. Antarctic Program. His duties shall require him to report and make recommendations to the Secretary of Defense on all matters pertaining . . ." He put the letter down and slumped in his chair.

178

Byrd's secretary looked at him with concern. "Anything wrong, Admiral?"

He forced a smile. "No. On the contrary, it's the best news I've had in my lifetime."

This was the victory, he thought—a permanent antarctic program and international participation. Too bad he was so tired . . . he should be celebrating, not panting as though he'd just walked off the gridiron. . . . That darned pain in his chest. What a nuisance! . . . Well, there were plans to be made for OPERATION DEEPFREEZE.

He sat up, leaned over his desk and reached for the telephone. "Give me Captain Dufek," he said.

Eight months later Byrd stood on the bridge of the icebreaker *Glacier*. Four-foot-thick pack ice crunched under the ship's bow. Lazy Weddell seals blinked at the noisy intruder and flocks of Adélie penguins skidded on their bellies across the ice to make way for the onrushing ship.

Like a nomad drinking from a spring after a long desert journey, Byrd inhaled the cold, heavy polar air. There, across the Ross Sea, was the Barrier and the wondrous beauty . . . there was Antarctica, land of his dreams come true.

The *Glacier* unloaded planes and supplies at McMurdo Sound, which would be the antarctic terminal for an air lift from New Zealand across twenty-four hundred miles of the Pacific.

Then the ship anchored at the Bay of Whales. A bright orange helicopter lifted Byrd and his aides from the *Glacier*'s deck. It hovered over Little America III and IV, then crabbed toward the site of Little America I and squatted down among the buried radio towers.

Byrd jumped out. "It's great to be back here," he said.

Paul Siple hauled a tall bamboo pole from the helicopter. He unfurled a United States flag, fastened it, and drove the pole into the snow.

Byrd and the rest of his party saluted.

"I'm a mayor of this place buried under sixty feet of ice and snow," Byrd said, laughing. "I'd like to linger here awhile, but we have things to do back at McMurdo. Let's go!"

Back at McMurdo the Navy's "Seabees" lived up to their fame, putting up buildings and unloading supplies flown to the air strip from New Zealand. Byrd was everywhere. With the eagerness of a schoolboy on a field trip, he asked questions, watched the tractors, planes, and helicopters.

" 'Morning, Admiral!" A bearded master sergeant with Air Force stripes called out.

Byrd squinted. "Say, is that you, Hendrik—Hendrik Dolleman?"

"Yes, sir! Remember my dog teams back in thirty-nine?" The sergeant grinned. "Well, I got myself new Huskies and we're back on the same old job!"

Within a month the old name "Little America" adorned a new base where seventy-three men would live. Plans were made to set up other permanent bases, including one on the South Pole. To survey that last base location, Byrd again flew to the Bottom of the World.

The four-engined Skymaster droned easily over Queen Maud's forbidding range. From the comfort of the heated cabin Byrd looked down on the formidable peaks and the still rivers of glaciers.

A crewman tapped him on the shoulders. "Chow

180

time, sir," he said. "Pork chops, French fries, and peas—lots of hot coffee."

Twenty-seven years ago, over that glacier, McKinley jettisoned almost three hundred pounds of food so that the *Floyd Bennett* would climb over the "Hump," Byrd thought.

He got up to walk to the cockpit and a hot pain shot through his chest. He leaned against the bulkhead, panting.

Paul Siple came to his side. "What's the matter? Are you hurt?"

"Nothing serious. All this comfort and warmth got me a little tired. I'll have a good rest when we get back."

With Phase I of OPERATION DEEPFREEZE completed, Byrd returned to the States to plan the remaining phase of the scientific assault and to check every detail of the latest recommendations.

Before going south on Phase II, Paul Siple came to say good-bye to Byrd. "I'll be looking forward to seeing you on the South Pole," he said. "I'm sorry you're not coming with us."

"So am I, Paul." Byrd grasped Siple's hand and held it. "But I'll be with you out there in spirit, if not in person . . . all this paper work . . . no end to it . . ."

"How is your pain?"

"Oh, it's all right. Probably an old injury acting up."

"I think you should see a doctor."

"A doctor! My foot!" Byrd straightened up. "I'm just tired of this darned paper work, that's all. As soon as the planning is finished, I shall go for a rest. And then I'll come to see you." He smiled. "I'll challenge you to a ski race, you'll see."

In November, 1956, Paul Siple and his crew started building their South Pole base. Air Force Globemasters air-lifted supplies from McMurdo air strip to the South Pole, dropping lumber, food, and machinery by parachute.

Paul Siple's progress report made Byrd smile. Comfortable huts for the eighteen men who would winter there . . . radar for tracking weather balloons, a photo lab, a special tower for observing the Southern Lights . . . direct radio contact by voice with any telephone number in the States. . . .

"Yes, Paul is a good man," Byrd muttered to himself. "He knows the importance of details out there. Well, perhaps I should take a rest before my next trip south."

In February, 1957, the Secretary of Defense awarded the Medal of Freedom to the sixty-eight-year-old Admiral Byrd. Ailing, Byrd was at his home at 9 Brimmer Street in Boston, and Admiral Burke, Chief of Naval Operations, made a special trip there to present the decoration.

"To Rear Admiral Richard Evelyn Byrd, U.S.N., Retired, for exceptional meritorious service to the United States," Burke read. "As Officer-in-Charge, U.S. Antarctic Programs since October, 1955, Admiral Byrd has demonstrated outstanding leadership and great skill. By virtue of his unparalleled experience, he has made a unique contribution to the Antarctic expeditions over the past three years, the development of permanent Antarctic legislation and international scientific understanding and good will. He has exercised his special talents in the promotion of the United States interests in the Antarctic with foreign countries and has personally laid the groundwork for the present large-scale Antarctic effort of the

United States. These accomplishments represent a lifetime of service which has encompassed unequaled exploits of skill, daring and imagination, including a flight across the Atlantic Ocean, the initial flights across the North and South Poles, and five historic expeditions to Antarctica. His actions and performances of these duties have been in keeping with the highest tradition of the United States Government Service. It gives me great pleasure to award Admiral Byrd the Medal of Freedom."

Burke frowned with mock seriousness. "And all I can add is that you should take things easy," he said. "You work too hard."

Byrd's blue-gray eyes sparkled as a smile softened his gaunt pale face. "I see you are in cahoots with my doctor. Well, nobody ever died from overwork, as the saying goes. Besides, there isn't much left to do anyway—just this report," he said, pointing to his desk. "Yes, George Dufek and Paul Siple have everything under control down there . . . they and all their men have helped fulfill my life's ambitions."

It was late evening, March 11, 1957, when Byrd finished proofreading his annual report. He leaned back and closed his eyes. His white, wavy hair contrasted sharply with the brown leather of the chair. He was tired, but now he could rest before his trip south.

The next day, short-wave radio at the South Pole base crackled a message: "Admiral Byrd died in his sleep last night, March 11 . . ."

The antarctic sun was setting over the polar horizon as the United States flag went down to half-mast. Paul Siple saluted. His breath turned into ice crystals that whispered a farewell prayer.

183

BIBLIOGRAPHY

BOOKS

Balchen, Bernt.   *Come North with Me,* E. P. Dutton & Co., New York, 1958

Byrd, Richard E.   *Alone,* G. P. Putnam's Sons, New York, 1938
Discovery, G. P. Putnam's Sons, New York, 1935
Exploring with Byrd, G. P. Putnam's Sons, New York, 1937
Little America, G. P. Putnam's Sons, New York, 1930
Skyward, Blue Ribbon Books, New York, 1928

Dufek, George J.   *Operation Deepfreeze,* Harcourt, Brace & Co., New York, 1957

Hobbs, Wm. H.   *Explorers of the Antarctic,* House of Field, 1941

Lindsay, Martin.   *The Epic of Captain Scott,* G. P. Putnam's Sons, New York, 1934

Miller, Francis T.   *The Fight to Conquer the Ends of the Earth,* John C. Winston Co., Philadelphia, 1930

Murphy, Char. J.   *Struggle,* Stokes, New York, 1928

Murray, James.   *Antarctic Days,* A. Melrose, London, 1913

O'Brien, John S.   *By Dog Sled for Byrd,* Thomas S. Rockwell Co., Chicago, 1931

Siple, Paul.   *Scout to Explorer,* G. P. Putnam's Sons, New York, 1936

MAGAZINES

All Hands, The Bureau of Naval Personnel Information Bulletin, Number 471, May, 1956, pp. 8-11; Number 488, September, 1957, pp. 59-63.

The National Geographic Magazine, Volume CX, Number 2, pp. 141-80; Volume CXII, Number 1, pp. 1-48; Volume CXII, Number 4, pp. 429-552.

INDEX

188

About the Author

MICHAEL GLADYCH was born in Warsaw, Poland, graduated from the Polish Air Force Academy and was commissioned a second lieutenant fighter pilot on September 1, 1939—the day Hitler invaded Poland. He flew in the French campaign during World War II, later joined the Royal Air Force and finally became a member of the U. S. Air Corps. He was decorated for distinguished service and bravery by the four governments which he served, and became a United States citizen when the war in Europe was over. Out of his wide experiences have come many articles, essays and books on various aspects of aviation. He now lives in Seattle, Washington, with his wife and two children.